THE ANATOMY
OF PLANTS

THE ANATOMY
OF PLANTS

P. FONT QUER

*Formerly, Professor of Botany and
Director of the Botanical Institute
Barcelona*

SCIENCE TODAY SERIES

HARPER & BROTHERS
Publishers   *New York*

HARPER & BROTHERS

49 East 33rd Street, New York 16, N.Y., USA

Translated by
D. H. R. NEWTON
from *Botánica Pintoresca*, first
published in Spain

CONTENTS

6

INTRODUCTION

Every part of the plant is composed of small unit forms, their boundaries being sometimes thin and sometimes thick, and—except in special cases—enclosing them completely on all sides. These spaces have been compared to the cells of a honeycomb, and when they take a prismatic shape they are really very much like them. It is because of this that they have been given the name of 'cells'.

Man, when he wants to erect any building that is not just a simple wattle-and-daub hut, or a wooden structure, starts by placing blocks of stone or some other hard material in an orderly fashion, one on top of the other, in such a way that the construction of the building is revealed in a pattern of vertical and horizontal lines. The cells which go to make up a part of a plant are arranged in much the same way. The cell is, then, the 'brick' or construction unit of plants—and, indeed, of all things organic. But it does not need an architect or builder to put it in place, for each unit is self-sufficient and places itself where it belongs, without the necessity of plans. The cells assume their correct order and arrangement in such a way that, according to the species, they grow into those wonderful pieces of living architecture—the trees, shrubs and flowers with which we are so familiar. Indeed, if it were not for our daily experience of these miracles we should stand spellbound before them.

As it is known that everything which lives, be it animal or vegetable, is composed of cells, we shall begin by studying these fundamental units of the organic world, limiting ourselves in this book to plant cells. Then we shall pass on to describe the structure and organs made of the different kinds of cells, and the mechanisms by which species of plants are propagated.

1

Cytology

THE CELL: CELLULAR MEMBRANE. Robert Hooke (1635-1703), the celebrated English physician, discovered plant cells by studying a piece of cork under the microscope. What he saw was lifeless matter—the skeletons of dead cells. The name 'cell' has remained and is in general use, but it is now applied not only to the dead cell walls but also to their living contents. When a cell is formed it is a living thing, engendered by a living parent cell. Some cells are predestined to die in a very short time; but others are capable of living for a very long time, sometimes for many years. The living part of the cell is contained within the cell wall, and that which Hooke discovered was merely the chamber where an elementary particle of living matter once lived. This latter is really the most important part of the cell.

Not all elementary living particles lodge in such finely built chambers. In cork, and, in general, in all vegetation to which we normally give the name of plants, this is so. We may think of them as 'doing time' in prison-cells, but without hope of liberation because the walls which form the minute dwelling are destined to form the tomb of the occupant.

But very simple plants exist which are formed of a single cell, invested with a very thin membrane. These live quite freely immersed in water, or in very damp places. Some, such as the motile cells of the myxomycetes, may be totally devoid of a membrane for at least a part of their lives, thus providing an extreme case of nakedness amounting to a paradox—they are cells without a cell.

In all cases, the newly-born cells have a thinner membrane than the old cells, because the membranes thicken with age. Some membranes become thick enough to seal off the cellular cavity completely and then all vital activity ceases therein. The woody part of trees called the 'heart-wood' is composed of a conglomeration of dead cells with very thick membranes, the latter having been converted into the the woody substance.

In general, in the plant kingdom the cells are characterised by having a well-strengthened membrane made of a substance called 'cellulose', which takes its name from the word 'cell'. In the seeds of the cotton plant, the strands which envelop it, the cotton, are formed from almost pure cellulose. In other cases, besides the actual cellulose— which has a formula $(C_6H_{10}O_5)_n$— the cellular membrane contains other similar substances (hemicelluloses, pectose, pectins, etc.), and when it is most mature, as in the adult cells, it may be formed of 'lignin' (in the cells of wood), of 'suberin' (in the bark of *Quercus suber* or cork oak), 'cutin' (in the co-called 'cuticle' which invests the external surface of young stems, leaves, etc.).

These substances, even when they have a similar chemical nature, have different properties, above all with regard to their permeability and to their toughness, which they impart to the membranes made up from them.

CYTOPLASM: CYTOPLASMIC MEMBRANE. Within the cellular membrane is found the living contents of the cell, a minute body of a viscous, semi-fluid material, which we may compare to the white of an egg. See Fig. 1. This material has been called the 'plasm' of the cell, or in a word, 'cytoplasm'. Its chemical nature is complex, but fundamentally it is composed of albuminoid matter.

In spite of its small size, the speck of plasm contained in a cell is not homogeneous even in its peripheral parts, which are composed of albumins and fatty material whose properties are of great importance to the life of the cell. The most important property is concerned with the selective permeability of the cytoplasm. This has the power of

A*

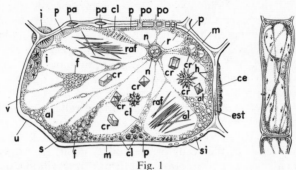

Fig. 1

Left: Idealised representation of a cell showing the cytoplasm and its products. At the top may be seen pores in the membrane, some of which, *po*, enable communication to be made with neighbouring cells, and others, *pa*, contain air spaces. The nucleus, *n*, exceedingly small, has two nucleoli, and is suspended by protoplasmic filaments which connect it with the parietal protoplasm, *p*; between the filaments large vacuoles, *v*, have been formed. In some of these may be seen small crystals of various forms, crystaloid, *cr*, or raphides, *raf*. The protoplasm contains chlorophyll, *cl*, amorphous or crystalized aleuron, *al*, inulin, *i*, oil, *h*, starch granules, *f*. The cellular membrane may be grooved, *est*, and allow waxy secretions, *ce*, to pass through it; siliceous concretions, *si*, may also be present in the membrane.

(*After* Baillon). *Right*: A cell of *Chara*, with the nucleus shown against the right-hand wall of the cellular membrane, the arrows indicating the direction in which the protoplasm circulates.

allowing, or not allowing, certain substances to pass through it; that is to say, it selects what may be admitted into the cell. This outer or peripheral zone does not have a clear inner boundary, but loses its character by degrees; nevertheless, it is called the 'cytoplasmic membrane'. Distinct from the cellular membrane, it is a living part of the cell and its semi-permeable nature is such that water may pass through it with ease, but not all other materials.

With all its chemical complexity, the appearance of cytoplasm, when seen through a microscope is uniform and clear as the white of egg, except that it contains certain tiny particles called 'chondriosomes' and 'microsomes' whose role in the cell has not been properly determined.

THE NUCLEUS: NUCLEAR MEMBRANE. Just as we find inside a peach or an apricot a sort of nut with a very hard, woody shell, which is the 'stone' or core of the fruit, so cytoplasm also contains a small mass, generally rounded and visible in sound and living cells, but much more apparent when we treat the cell with suitable reagents which stain it intensely. This small mass has been given the name of 'nucleus', a contracted form of the Latin *nuculeus*, which in turn comes from *nux, nucis* a nut. See Fig. 2.

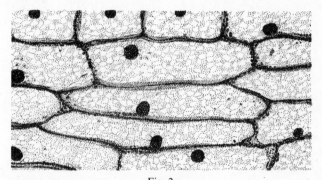

Fig. 2
Epidermal cells from an onion skin, elongated and with the nucleus quite visible. (*From a photomicrograph by* Pluvier.)

The stone of a fruit contains within its shell its most important constituent—that is to say, the seed; and in like manner to the interior of the nucleus has been reserved transcendent functions, since not only does it rule over the life of the cell but it also holds the inherited characters of its progenitors, transmitting them to its own descendants according to strict laws of nature. Within the cell the individuality of the nucleus is so complete that it is separated from the main cytoplasm mass by another special membrane, the 'nuclear membrane'.

The cytoplasm, with the nucleus and with all that it contains, constitutes the basic biological unit, the cell being considered as a living and working elementary entity. It is also called the 'protoplast', a word which, etymologically, means the 'first founder', or—if you will—a sort of Adam of all that lives on the earth, the fundamental principle of all organic beings.

CHROMOSOMES. In reality, the stains that we use to show up the nucleus do not stain it uniformly, and certain small particles, usually of an elongated form, soak up the colour greedily and leave the rest of the nucleus only partly stained. Consequently, these bodies have received the name of 'chromosomes', a word meaning 'coloured bodies'. This property of the chromosomes is identical with that of a substance called 'chromatin', which contains timonucleic acid. This acid retains colours of a basic chemical nature, and these are therefore commonly used to stain the nucleus for microscopic examination.

The number of chromosomes is constant in the cells of each animal or vegetable species and in them are located the hereditary characteristics. If the nucleus is in control of the life of the protoplast, and then, at a given moment, transfers its faculties to its progeny, it would seem that its power is mainly contained in the chromosomes.

CHROMONEME. The chromosome itself is not a homogeneous body. When it is analysed by an advanced microscopic technique, a chromosome is seen to have the form of a coiled thread rather like a corkscrew, the 'chromoneme', which is embedded in a very delicate sheath called the 'matrix'. The chromoneme is the most important part of the chromosome, and when the right moment arrives, it splits longitudinally into two exactly equal parts, the 'chromatids'.

CHROMOMERES AND GENES. In the chromonemes one can see certain intensely stained granulations arranged in lines, and these are called 'chromomeres'. Some chromomeres are quite thick and closely bunched together; others are finer and less crowded. On these latter are situated the elementary genetic units which are designated by the

name of 'genes'. They are composed of nucleoproteins—
that is to say, of proteins and nucleic acid. A gene is, then,
a material particle capable of transmitting a character, or
of handing down its properties to its descendants.

PLASTIDS. In the protoplasts of plant cells (except in
bacteria and other organisms, most of which live at the
expense of others) are found minute bodies called 'plastids'.
At first, in recently formed cells, the plastids are very small
and uncoloured, hardly visible. In adult cells they reach
greater dimensions and, especially if the cell gets the necessary light, the plastids become coloured a beautiful green.
Plastids with this green colour are called 'chloroplasts',
the colour being due to an organic substance called
'chlorophyll'. This has a very complicated chemical
formula, and is an elaborate combination of many atoms
of carbon, hydrogen and oxygen, linked with four atoms
of nitrogen and one of magnesium.

Plastids do not always become green chloroplasts. Sometimes they take a yellow-orange hue, something like a
carrot, because instead of chlorophyll they contain 'caro-
tin' or the bright yellow 'xanthophyll', etc. For this reason
the coloured plastids, whatever their hue, have the general
names of 'chromoplastids' or 'chromatophores'—that is,
'bearers of pigments'. The carrot itself contains chromatophores of an orange colour in its cells, and many flowers,
including some yellow ones, are coloured in the same way.
If they should be in any way deprived of light, plastids
remain colourless, or very nearly so, and then they are
called 'leucoplastids'. Normally, leucoplastids are the least
common type of chromatophore.

If the nucleus controls the life of the protoplast and
transmits hereditary characteristics, the chloroplasts carry
out a function no less important. This is due to the presence in its substance of the green pigment chlorophyll,
round which is centred the photochemical activity of the
cell. This, as we shall see later on, consists primarily of the
synthesis of an organic substance, starch, from two in-

organic substances, water and carbon dioxide, a combination carried out with the aid of light-energy from the sun. This is why we find small granules of starch inside the chloroplasts, especially after a bright day in favourable conditions of temperature and humidity.

The granules of starch thus formed are converted little by little into glucose, which, being soluble, can disperse. Generally, after a sufficiently long night, the chloroplasts may be completely free of glucose before the day dawns. Leucoplasts, on the other hand, can reconvert the glucose into starch—the 'starch reserve'; this is then stored as in the potato or in rice grains.

VACUOLES AND CELL SAP. In newly formed cells, the cytoplasm fills the whole cavity; but this is not so in adult cells, and even less in old ones. The cytoplasmic contents do not grow at the same rate as the young cell grows; consequently, the cytoplasm cannot continue to occupy the entire space without producing small cavities called 'vacuoles'. These are not really completely empty spaces however, because the cell absorbs water which, together with certain substances in solution, constitutes the 'cell sap'. In effect, we have vacuoles, left by the cytoplasm as the cell expands, filled with this sap. In the oldest cells, the cytoplasm is normally adherent to the cellular membrane, and a large central vacuole is thus formed. In some cases, this cytoplasmic layer is so thin that it can only be perceived with difficulty. The nucleus may also be found next to the membrane, or more towards the centre of the cell. In the latter case it will be held in position by cytoplasmic filaments. However, even though, owing to its thinness, the parietal cytoplasmic layer is very nearly invisible, it is very easy to bring it into view. It is sufficient to place the cell in a solution of common salt to see how the protoplast, reinvested with its thin cytoplasmic membrane, leaves the cell wall and tends to crowd into the centre of the cell. This phenomenon is very easy to explain if we remember that the cytoplasmic membrane, being semi-permeable, allows water to pass through it but not salt. The drop of sodium chloride solution we may put on the slide used to cover the cell can pass through the cell wall but not the cytoplasmic membrane. The cell sap, on the other hand, being almost pure water passes through the latter, and as it reaches the outside of the cell the turgidity which it had caused in the protoplast now disappears, and the protoplast, like a deflated balloon, tends to shrink into the centre of the cellular cavity.

The cell sap contains very small amounts of various salts, glucose and other sugars, albuminoid material and organic acids. All these substances are considered to be always present in it. But it sometimes contains other things, among them alkaloids in many plants and anthocyanin pigments in blue or violet flowers. Some of these substances may be of use to the plant; others are by-products of plant metabolism and may be of no value at all to the organism. Among these last are frequently small crystals of calcium oxalate, elongated like needles and arranged in small bundles known as 'raphides'. In many cases the vacuoles do not contain cell sap, but oils, essences, resins etc.

DETAILS OF THE CELLULAR MEMBRANE. The young cell begins to grow regularly until it reaches the size of the adult cell. The membrane, however, extends by dilating, or by intercalating fresh material in the original cell wall. While the membrane is increasing in size and expanding, it begins to thicken, and in many cases its thickness increases even more after development of its outer surface has ceased. This increase is achieved by successive deposits of protoplasm on the internal surface of the membrane, which thus gains in size at the expense of the cellular cavity.

The increase in thickness may be evenly distributed over the entire internal surface, which may therefore thicken in a uniform manner, but frequently it does not happen like this. That is to say, the thickness of some parts is increased by continued deposition of new layers, while at other points no deposits are made. In this way holes are produced—

concavities at the bottom of which we still find the original cellular membrane unaltered. The holes are of varying form and position but, in general, they are constant for each species of plant and cell.

If, on the other hand, the areas in which increase of thickness is taking place are limited, the result is something quite different. Instead of holes, protuberances at the points of thickening are seen, and these may be of varying shapes, resembling warts, barbs, screw-threads, etc. They are especially noticeable in the cells called pollen grains, produced from the stamens of flowers. Sometimes they adopt characteristic forms and may all be of the same type, so that they can be used to identify the pollen grains even though it may not be known from which plant they have been taken.

2

Histology

CELL TISSUES. In the seventeenth century Robert Hooke noticed that plant parts cut into sections and studied under the microscope revealed cells joined together to form sheets, with the cell membranes marking out spaces of varying shape, very much like the weft and warp of some fabric. Towards the end of the century these sheets of connected cells began to be called 'tissues', a word derived from the French *tissu*, meaning 'woven'. The word seemed well chosen and still remains in botanical and zoological scientific terminology. In botany, we call any homogeneous group of connected cells which, as a rule, contribute by their activity to the fulfilment of a common function, a 'tissue'.

By stating that the group must be homogeneous we are trying to emphasize that the cells making up a tissue should have a common origin. In other words, when we study how the cells were formed and where they came from, sooner or later we find the cell or primordial tissue which can be considered as the progenitor of the tissue being examined. In other cases, when the connected group of cells originates from separate cells not previously united, then we consider the tissue as an illegitimate or false one, even though the original cells are all exactly similar. This happens, for example, in the spore-bearing mechanisms of the fungi, known by the name of 'setae', and also in all those cases which result in an accumulation of cells without specialisation, and without any apparent reason for being together.

The branch of morphology which deals with cellular tissues and studies their origins and composition has been

17

given the name of 'histology'. The first part of this word is derived from the Greek *histos*, which means a tissue—that is to say, a fabric. However, the meaning that has been given to the word histology does not bear any relationship to the art of textile-weaving, for histologists employ it solely in connection with an organism. When we wish to refer to the constituents of a cellular tissue we call them 'histic'; and those parts of the plant which are not composed of connected cells are said to have an 'anhistic' structure.

In the so-called higher plants—that is to say, those which have flowers—tissue formation reaches a high level of variations and possibilities, and it is in such plants that we see tissues at their largest and in their greatest numbers and most diverse forms. It is also here that we see collections of cells unitedly carrying out functions which a single isolated cell may perform by itself. But in this case the work is much more difficult than that of the single cell. In the first place, the isolated cell lives in water, or in very damp places where it would always have water within its reach, whereas the plant which lives in earth has to solve for itself the problems of acquiring and distributing water, and avoiding losses which could prove fatal to it. Again, such a plant must support itself, either erect or trailing along the ground, but always needing a certain firmness of substance. For each of these needs, and for many others, specialised tissues have to be provided in order to maintain the functions of the others.

DIVISION OF LABOUR. The isolated and submerged cell is self-supporting inasmuch as it can perform all the work necessary to its well-being. For example, it must provide insulation from its surrounding medium, water absorption, synthesis of basic nutritional substances, and so on. On the other hand, in the multi-cellular plants there is a veritable 'division of labour', because each one of its specialised tissues is in charge of looking after at least one of these vital functions.

ORIGIN OF PLANT TISSUES. Because every cell is derived from another, preformed cell, it can be inferred that tissues are engendered by cellular procreation. As happens in the more simple species, if from each cell two are formed and then the mother and daughter cells separate immediately afterwards in order to repeat the same operation, no tissue is formed. But sometimes, the new generations of cells, which may multiply with great rapidity, remain attached to their progenitors by the viscosity of the membranes, and in this manner they come to form filaments, sheets or masses of varying thickness which may give the appearance of cellular tissue. In reality however, we cannot recognise them as tissues proper, because there is no division of labour among the cells of the mass, and all cells carry out the same functions. The first indication that cells are doing specialised work is seen when a cell or cells in a primary cellular group attaches the latter to some kind of support. This duty of anchoring the cell-group at once demands that the cell concerned be different from its fellows.

In plants of a more upright structure, the origins of tissues become much more complicated; but in all cases there exist the generative cells distributed in various patterns on whose activity the structure of the plant depends, as we shall see later on.

ORGANS AND THE INTRACELLULAR ORGANISATION. The word 'organ' comes from the Greek *organon*, and its fundamental meaning is that of an instrument or tool for the purposes of work. Whether or not the Greeks possessed musical instruments also called organs, it is at least certain that Aristotle had bestowed the same name on those parts of the body which perform definite functions. In botany, an organ is a part of a plant, generally multi-cellular, which discharges one or more duties.

When the cell has reached its full size and is composed of the cytoplasmic membrane, the nucleus, the plastids and other living elements, each one acting according to its character and exercising a distinct function, it is clear that, from the point of view of its activities, it can be compared with a multicellular organism. It would seem, therefore, that these diminutive work-units within the cell should also be referred to as 'organs'.

ORGANIC APPARATUSES. Two or more organs of an individual may co-ordinate to perform a function more generalised than that of either of them separately; when this happens the group of organs forms an 'apparatus'. The assimilating apparatus, for instance, comprises the green parts of the plant, all the leaves, the bracts if any, the green parts of the stem and branches, etc.

The intracellular organization may also form apparatuses; thus there exists the so-called chromatic appatus constituted by the group of chromosomes in the cell.

SYSTEMS. A 'system' is again more complex than an apparatus, for it may consist of several apparatuses, as in the conducting system. This begins with the roots, which absorb aqueous solutions from the soil and conduct them to the stem, which then takes over and delivers them to the branches. These conduct the solutions to the leaves, where they are distributed among a maze of small veins. From here, the watery sap enriched by the nourishment manufactured in the leaf, is conducted back again down the stem and through the roots, until it reaches the tiniest root-hairs. The object of this is the transportation of the vital plant juices, and it is accomplished by means of many diverse organs and apparatuses co-ordinated into a 'system'.

ORGANIZATION AND ORGANISM. When cells arrange themselves to conform with a functional plan, grouping themselves into tissues and organs, they are said to be 'organized'. The final result of this organization is a living unit or 'organism'. From our description of the conducting system there emerges the conception of an individual plant as a group of related organs. Should one of these fail the rest become weakened. This solidarity of the organism does not lie simply in the physical union of its parts, but is based on more intimate connections.

CONNECTIONS BETWEEN PROTOPLASTS: PLASMODESMAS. The membranes which separate contiguous cells are very thin when they are newly formed, as we have already explained, and as they get older they increase in thickness. If these membranes were to thicken uniformly they would finish by isolating each cell in a tissue from its fellows, but in general this does not happen.

We have already pointed out that as a cell wall thickens, small holes or canals are left which communicate with a neighbouring cell. When two of these canals face each other they form a single channel which possesses a fine dividing membrane near its centre. This was the membrane which originally separated the cells when they were first formed and is normally composed of very thin cellulose.

As a rule, fine filaments of protoplasm called 'plasmodesmas' connect adjoining cells across this thin partition, which separates the bodies of the protoplasts.

INTERCELLULAR SPACES. Neighbouring cells in a tissue which is in the process of formation are so packed that no spaces are to be seen between them. When you examine a section of such a tissue under the microscope, it looks like a diminutive pavement of perfectly laid blocks. However, an inspection of the same tissue in the adult form shows a very different aspect. The cells still have the appearance of being paving stones, but this time they seem to be very badly fitted; the small gaps which occur between some of them are known as 'intercellular spaces'.

There are some very narrow intercellular spaces called 'meatuses' common in almost every kind of tissue. But sometimes they are larger and are wider than the cells themselves, in which case they are called 'chambers', the name 'hiatuses' or 'gaps' being reserved for those which are even bigger. Usually, chambers and gaps are formed by the disintegration of a varying number of cells.

VARIETIES OF TISSUES
Embryonic or Meristematic Tissues

Tissues in process of formation are called 'embryonic tissues', and sometimes 'meristems'. The cells forming them are relatively small, and have a thin membrane and a proportionately large nucleus. These cells reproduce very rapidly by division, one becoming two, the two, in their turn, becoming four, and so on, and at the same time the size of the cells increases.

When a single cell begins to form a new multicellular plant and starts dividing, the compact grouping of cells which first appears is known as the 'primary meristem'. Since the organism may be composed of several parts or members, a number of focal points appear in this primary meristem, each being related to a particular part of the young plant. Thus, concentrations of meristem are found at the extreme tips of the stem, the branches and the roots, and from them are derived the distinctive shapes and forms of these parts by differentiating tissues and their corresponding organs.

Even in tissues which may be considered adult, it sometimes happens that cells with very thin membranes recover this juvenile faculty of dividing and behave meristematically to produce new cells. In their mass, such rejuvenated cells constitute a 'secondary meristem'.

Adult Tissues

When the organism reaches the adult stage, the tissues composing it—also adult—have cells with the membrane more or less thickened and separated by meatuses. Lacking meristems, they have relatively small nuclei and quite distinct vacuoles. Such cells have reached maturity and are incapable of further division. The main types of adult tissues are as follows.

PARENCHYMA. The Ancient Greek anatomists distinguished between two classes of flesh: muscular flesh, somewhat fibrous, which they called *sarx* (genitive *sarkos*, from which we get the word 'sarcophagus'), and the substance of the viscera—liver and lungs, for example—to which they gave the name of *paregchyma*. The 'non-fibrous' flesh of plants, is generally composed of cells as long as, or only a little longer, than they are wide, separated by meatuses. They have thin cellulose membranes with tiny perforations which maintain communication between protoplasts, with the protoplasm adherent to the membrane and surrounding a central vacuole, and with the plastids distributed in various ways. Such tissue is called the 'phytoparegchyma' or 'plant parenchyma'. It appears to be scattered throughout the plant, in the roots, stems and leaves, and constitutes a sort of fundamental tissue of the organism, ready to discharge a multitude of duties.

When the parenchyma is located near the surface of the plant in such a way that light reaches it through the cells separating it from the outside, chlorophyll is formed in the plastids and they are converted into chloroplastids. Thus we have 'chlorophyllic parenchyma', and it is here that the photosynthesis of starch takes place. The deeper parenchyma tissues, and those less subjected to light, do not have this green pigmentation, and should they happen to contain starch it is because it has migrated there in the form of soluble glucose from chlorophyllic parenchyma, and then been reconstituted. This second type is called 'storage parenchyma', because it is here that the plant's reserves are stored. The most usual form of plant reserve is starch, but other substances, such as fats and albuminoids, may be stored in tissue of this type.

With the same object, that is of storage, we have 'aquiferous' or water-bearing parenchyma, which is indispensable during long periods of drought to such plants as have to rely on water for their survival. 'Aerated' or air-bearing parenchyma does not store air in its cells, but allows it to circulate with great facility due to the considerable develop-

ment of its meatuses. This is an important function and
deserves the attention drawn to it here.

Although the transportation of liquids absorbed by the
plant, and of the sap made from them, is chiefly effected by
means of special vessels which we shall study later, it is at
least certain that some cells of parenchymatous tissue allow
plant juices to circulate through them, although very slowly. This 'conducting parenchyma' is located in various
parts of the plant, and is commonly characterised by its
cells being elongated in the direction of flow.

There still exist other kinds of parenchyma of lesser
importance, varying in their structure as well as in the
tasks they perform, but we need not consider them here.

SUPERFICIAL TISSUES. Plants which do not live under
water require protection against the hazards of their
environment and especially against drying out. In those
climates where rain is frequent throughout the year, and
the air is saturated or nearly so with water vapour, a simple
layer of surface cells is protection enough, and they can be
as thin as circumstances warrant. But in those regions of
the globe having long periods of drought the problem of
defending the plant against water-loss becomes very serious
indeed. In every such case the protection needed is supplied
by the 'superficial tissues'.

The most important of these is the 'epidermal tissue' or,
more simply, the 'epidermis'. Plants do not have a skin or
hide like animals, but there is a membrane enveloping the
entire plant, and because it plays a similar role to the skin
of animals the word 'epidermis' has been appropriated for
it. Seeing that its whole aim is to avoid water-loss by
evaporation, or at least to reduce this to a minimum, its
cells are designed to fit as closely together as possible without any intercellular spaces, these conditions being essential since usually the epidermis consists of a single layer of
cells. The most efficient epidermal cells are those which
have their borders sinuous and indented, and with the
projections of one cell inserted in the indentations of its

neighbours, the whole being perfectly fitted together like
a jig-saw puzzle as shown in Fig. 3.

Epidermal cells, when seen in longitudinal section, that
is to say, when cut perpendicularly to the external surface,
have little thickness, from which we deduce that the
epidermis is little more than a maze of interlocking sinuous
cell walls. The external surfaces of the epidermal cells are
thickened according to the plant's environment; that is to

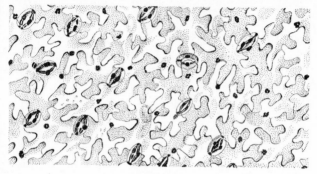

Fig. 3

Epidermal cells of valerian, showing the contortions of the cell boundaries
and numerous stomata. (*From a photomicrograph by* Poilpot).

say, according to whether it is expected to withstand
drought or to exist in a humid atmosphere. But, with the
exception of the roots, epidermal tissue is always protected by a continuous layer of 'cutin', a substance which
is practically impermeable to water and gases. This coating,
not cellular but anhistic, is called the 'cuticle'. Quite
frequently, a deposit of wax is formed over the cuticle
which deflects water which falls on the leaves or stems of
plants thus protected; this deposit reinforces the sealing
already achieved by the epidermis and the cuticle. The
glaucous colour of cabbage is produced by a fine coating
of wax which may easily be removed by simply passing the
fingers over the surface of the leaves.

A waterproof and air-tight covering such as we have
described would be disastrous to the life of the plant if it

were not for certain ingenious devices incorporated in the epidermal tissue. The plant, having been protected from water loss, would at the same time be deprived of air, and this would prove fatal to it if adequate provision were not made. The plant needs the carbon dioxide in the air, and it does not in fact die because the epidermis is perforated, not with simple holes but with openings that can be opened and closed according to the plant's requirements. This is done in an efficient and rapid way and regulates the intake and expulsion of air. These tiny openings, which resemble microscopic mouths, each one having two lips, are called 'stomata' (singular 'stoma'). The stomata open when there is no danger that water will be lost, and shut when there is. See Fig. 4.

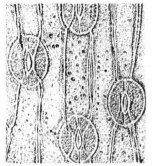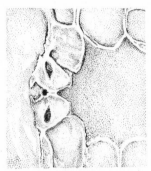

Fig. 4

Left: Group of stomata on a leaf with the openings or pores distinctly shown. *Right*: Longitudinal section of the underside of a leaf with the sub-stomatal air-chamber well shown. Highly magnified. (*After* Francé).

The stomata are not, then, simple epidermal fissures, but complicated arrangements consisting of two kidney-shaped cells joined at their ends and having their concave sides opposing each other. These are the 'guard cells' and their action is automatic, sometimes leaving a very small aperture and sometimes closing altogether.

The guard cells of a stoma act according to the internal pressure of the cell contents. When they are turgid the aperture opens, and if they are flaccid it closes. When it is open, the aperture enables communication to take place between the exterior of the plant and the 'substomatal airchamber', which in turn communicates with the intercellular spaces of the plant.

Stomata are normally found on the leaves and chiefly on their undersides.

TRICHOMES. The word 'trichome' means a hair or group of hairs, and comes from the Greek *thrix* (genitive *trichos*), hair. When we use the word trichome in botany we are referring not only to hairs but to many other epidermal processes of various forms, both unicellular and multicellular. We can see that trichomes constitute another form of protection for the plant, since an epidermis covered with a layer of hairs or scales, sometimes quite dense, possesses yet another defence against water losses and against the effects of excessive exposure to the sun.

Trichomes have their origin on the epidermis and arise from their own cells. The simplest is composed of a single cell, sometimes relatively short, and in such cases is called a 'papilla'. Others are multicellular and their cells are arranged in lines either single or branched. There are also squamose trichomes which are formed by multicellular laminae, rather like small scales. See Fig. 5.

Any part of the plant may have hairs; but the hairs on the roots have a particular function of their own, that of absorbing water from the soil. They are located at the end of the young root and have a short life.

Hairs vary considerably as to length, thickness and rigidity. When they are very stiff and rough to the touch we say they are 'bristly'; in other cases they are as smooth as silk so we call them 'silky'. There are also hairs which end in a small gland full of an oily substance or essence, and these are termed 'glandular hairs'. Finally, there are others, very rigid, sharp-pointed and fragile, like those on the nettle, and these are called 'urticant hairs' because if touched by an animal they break off short and stick in its

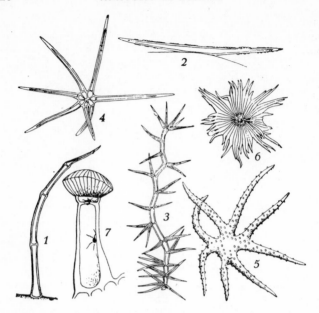

Fig. 5

Plant hairs. 1, Simple and multicellular (*Sideritis hirsuta*). 2, Simple navicular (boat-shaped) (*Alyssum maritimum*). 3, Branched hair (*Verbascum*). 4, Star-shaped (*Althaea rosea*). 5, Star-shaped (*Alyssum alyssoides*). 6, Scale-like (*Elaeagnus angustifolia*). 7, Glandular hair (*Verbascum blattaria*). All highly magnified. (*No.* 1 *after* Murbeck).

skin, causing some irritation. This is due partly to the jagged edge of the broken point, which remains in the skin, and partly to the contents of the hair cell, which is an irritant and is injected into the flesh as by a hypodermic syringe.

SKELETAL TISSUE. The name 'skeletal tissue' is given to all that conglomeration of plant substance which goes towards supporting the plant. The rigidity of a tall stem is due to a good skeletal system. In the vegetable kingdom, with its numerous differentiated cells, the skeletal tissues may be said to carry out the functions of the bony skeleton of vertebrates. They comprise many kinds of tissues, all purely mechanical.

'Sclerenchyma' is a type of sclerotic or hardened paren-chyma, and is composed of cells having their membranes uniformly thickened and lignified. It is a good supporter of vegetable organs both during growth and when they reach full development. It is composed of cells which are either little or no longer than they are broad, the 'scleren-chymatous cells', or elongated and spindle-shaped, the 'sclerenchymatous fibres'. As they reach full maturity, that is to say after their membranes have ceased to thicken, both cells and fibres no longer have living elements; they are dead cells. The very long threads from the stems of flax or ramie are nothing but sclerenchymatous fibres, and these, after having been separated from the surrounding vegetable tissue, are used in industry.

'Collenchyma' differs from sclerenchyma in that the thickening of the cell-walls are not uniform; some portions of the membrane do not change while others thicken only slightly. On the other hand, when it does thicken it does so very markedly, particularly at or near the angular parts of the membrane. The thinner parts of the cell or collen-chymatous fibre allow passage of plant juices so that there is circulation, whereas the sclerenchyma becomes com-pletely sealed off. As a consequence, collenchyma remains living and keeps relatively soft and of a grass-like texture, and the cell-walls do not lignify. It is especially adapted for herbaceous vegetation which needs this kind of support for its proper development. Thus, the quadrilateral stems of the labiate plants (dead-nettles) generally have a thread of collenchyma running along each of their four edges.

Sometimes we come across isolated cells or groups of cells which have their membranes thickened and lignified. They give 'body' to the tissues and in some cases make them very solid indeed, as, for instance, in the 'stone cells' of nut shells, and in the stones of olives, cherries, peaches and other drupes.

This is a brittle hardness, inflexible and strong. In contrast, the sclerenchymatous fibres, while conferring on the stem a certain degree of rigidity, at the same time give it the necessary flexibility to curve or bend and afterwards to recover its normal position. This is of importance when, for example, the plant is buffeted by strong winds.

CONDUCTING TISSUES. We have already shown how the water absorbed from the soil by the roots, or the sap itself, may pass through simple parenchymatous cells; but this is done so slowly that it is insufficient for the vital requirements of the plant. However, this disadvantage is overcome by means of the 'conducting tissues', which are adapted to supply all the plant organs with the water, juices and other liquids they may need. The extreme specialisation of these tissues as transporters of watery liquids is apparent when their structure is examined. We are, naturally, talking about land-plants because it is primarily in these that the problems of an efficient water supply become of the highest importance.

In effect, conducting tissues are composed of elongated tubes down which sap descends and up which water ascends, just like a pipeline carrying oil or water. The needs of the plant dictate the direction in which the liquids must flow, and the conducting tissues are adapted to ensure this.

Water (and the substances dissolved in it), after having been absorbed by the roots, must ascend to the branches and leaves. It does so by means of 'vessels', which are long cells arranged in threadlike formation, one after the other. They do not live long. Shortly after they are formed their membranes thicken and the protoplasts die. At first, the cells are separated from each other by slanting partitions placed across the axis of the tube formed; but quite soon these transverse partitions open at their centres to make a pore through which the watery fluids may pass on their way up from the roots to the very tip of the plant.

The walls of the tube-like cells composing the finished

'pipeline' may be seen to be thickened in a variety of ways. Some are formed of threads arranged like transverse rings, others have threads which spiral their way around the cell-wall, others again stand out in relief as a sort of woven net, and so on, but all these devices tend to impart great strength to the vessels. The presence of vessels is most important for the plant, since, when it is in full growth, water is absorbed in large quantities in order to maintain hydrostatic equilibrium; the plant would be in danger if this should be upset due to excessive transpiration or water-loss.

The side walls of the vessels are also perforated, but with very small pores called 'pits', simple or bordered, through which the vessel may pass liquids to neighbouring cells, or receive liquids from them, according to the varying pressures occurring between the vessel and the surrounding tissues. Sometimes these pits have an elongated form, and when they occur one above the other in the vessel wall they make a kind of ladder-structure and the vessels in which they occur are therefore called 'scalariform' vessels.

There are other vessels in which the partitions, more or less oblique, never disappear; communication is established along the vessel by means of the small holes with which the partitions are provided. These elements have been given the name of 'tracheids' and they take the place of true vessels in pine trees, spruce, cedars and other gymnosperms.

Finally, there is another type of specialised conducting tissue, tubes composed of lengthened cells with their membranes either exactly transversal or only slightly oblique, and with open pores. In contrast to the tracheids and vessels, these long cells are living and they allow the synthesized sap to flow through the pores on its journey down from the leaves to the roots *via* the stem. Because the transverse membranes of these cells are perforated like sieves, they are called 'sieve tubes'. The side walls of these tubes rarely lignify; they are made of cellulose in the same way as most other living plant cells and they possess turgidity due to this vitality. In most cases, sieve tubes renew themselves with each life cycle of the plant.

The vessels and the sieve tubes generally form congregations of conducting tissues which are known as 'vascular bundles'. In young plants the tracheids and vessels run together, separate from the sieve tubes, forming a sort of mixed bundle.

Circulation of liquids is thus seen to take place by means of two distinct kinds of conducting tissue; the raw materials of sap, such as water and mineral substances from the ground, rise and flow through the vessels, while the sap itself, along with other organic material, descends *via* the sieve tubes from the topmost leaves down to the lowest roots.

SECRETING CELLS AND TISSUES. The secreting tissues may be found isolated or grouped in various ways, sometimes forming tubes of considerable length and sometimes coming from a single embryonic cell which develops lengthwise as the plant grows. Again, the secreting elements may be formed from cells of varying and distinct origin uniting later to make up a tissue, some of the cells combining after the dissolution of the separating membranes. There are some cells, whether isolated or grouped, rounded or elongated, in which are deposited certain materials produced by the plant itself as a result of the chemical action inside the protoplast — that is, as a result of metabolism. Mucilages and gums are among these substances, as well as essential oils, resins and gum-resins, alkaloids, tannin, calcium oxalate crystals, etc. In the tubular secretory cells of many plants, principally in the spurges, a fluid material looking like milk is found. This is called 'latex' and the tubes secreting it are called 'lactiferous' tubes.

GLANDULAR TISSUES AND ELEMENTS. As well as the products of the secretory elements which remain shut up within their respective cells, there are diverse substances produced from other cells but ejected from them as soon as they are formed. These products may be merely left outside the cell wall, or they may be ejected from the plant body altogether, while in some cases they accumulate in the intercellular spaces. Secretory cells, those in which are deposited products of metabolism, have a very precarious existence and may be already dead, but, on the other hand, the glandular cells are living cells which expel waste products.

This type of cell often constitutes 'glandular tissue'; it may often be epidermal and is then called 'glandular epithelium'. In other instances it is the actual epidermal cell which produces a glandular hair, and this may be of a great number of shapes and types, either sessile or attached by a more or less elongated peduncle. There are also glandular cells in the heart of the plant, or tissues of the same kind surrounded by other tissues. Such cells empty their secretions into special recipients of various forms and origins. The substances produced are of an infinite variety. When a leaf of rue or hypericum (Perforate St. John's wort) is held up to the light, the numerous little clear points which are seen are so many small containers of essential oils produced by the activity of glandular cells.

3

Anatomy of Vegetative Organs

Plants are built up of cells which are grouped together to form organs, and normally a very great number of cells are required to make the tissues necessary for the performance of any particular function. When a solitary cell can bring to completion all the vital functions of the individual, vegetative as well as reproductive, the work is not done by organs but by the microscopic components of the cell protoplast. For this reason very many unicellular plants—for example, the bacteria—do not have organs.

Cell colonies, although they have a constant form and characteristics, also lack true organs; each one of the cells which go to form a colony is working on its own account, so to speak, without any kind of functional dependance on its neighbours. The *Coenobia*, for example, which are colonies of a distinctive shape and which conserve this shape throughout their existence, do not have any definite organs. But sometimes, among the *Coenobia*, a cellular differentiation may be noticed which might be considered as the rudiments of limbs or branches—incipient organs of a most elementary nature. If, in any one of these cellular groups, some of the cells differ from the others, by virtue of their position, then we have to recognise that in this purely morphological differentiation we have the foreshadowing of limbs, although they are still quite inoperative. When, to this morphological differentiation, there is added a corresponding functional property, then function begins and the organ, while still elementary, is now in existence. A filamentous colony of *Algae*, with its basal cell or cells containing no chlorophyll but developed in such a manner as to form a filament attached to some support, provides us with a good example of an organ in its most elementary stage of evolution.

Differentiation of cell and tissue function reaches its peak in the so-called higher plants with well defined and very complex organs. They begin their existence as simple primordial or embryonic tissue, and step by step grow and take shape until the adult plant is formed with all the organs necessary for its subsistence and the propagation of its kind. At this stage we say that the plant has a 'plant body' which has originated from an embryo, and all such plants which possess stems, leaves, etc. (although they may not have true roots) are grouped together under the name of 'Embryophyta'.

The Embryophyta are distinguished from the 'Thallophyta', which are plants which have no true stems and leaves (or roots), although they sometimes possess quite complex organs which may closely resemble leafy or stem-like structure. Such a plant body is called a 'thallus'.

Both in the Embryophyta and the Thallophyta, the functions of the organism fall into two categories: vegetative and reproductive. The vegetative functions are responsible for developing and maintaining the individual plant, and the reproductive functions are designed to perpetuate it. Both functions are carried out by their respective organs. In this book we are concerned chiefly with the higher plants and their organs and shall not, therefore, describe the Thallophyta in detail.

The vegetative organs of the plant body start by becoming differentiated within the embryo. When an embryo is large enough, for example in the seed of the broad bean or kidney bean, it can be examined quite easily with the naked eye (or with the aid of a lens) after the two halves or 'cotelydons' which form the seed have been soaked and then separated. The embryo can be seen at one end of the seed. At its point will be noticed a prolonged part which is the small primordial root or 'radicle', set to one side. The two cotyledons are attached at the upper end of the

radicle, one being inserted on each side. They do not, however, arise exactly from the radicle itself but from a short
stem-like structure called the 'hypocotyl'.

Above the attachment of the cotyledons we can see a
pair of leaves in miniature, facing each other and having
small veins in relief. If we discount the cotyledons, these
will be the plant's first pair of leaves as it develops, and
between them is located the centre from which the shoot
of the new plant will spring. The pair of opposing leaves
protecting this apical bud, together with it, comprise the
'plumule' or rudimentary shoot. An embryo of the higher
plants, then, consists of this primordial shoot with its
plumule, prolonged at its base to form the radicle, the
forerunner of the future root.

As the bean germinates, the root sinks down into the soil
and the stem rises into the air. At this stage we can appreciate that the cotyledons do not originate as near the root
as at first may appear from inspection of the seed, and we
can see that the hypocotyl represents that part of the
rudimentary stem between the cotyledons and the base of
the root. The part that rises upwards, and which may be
seen between the cotyledons and the first leaf or pair of
leaves, is called the 'epicotyl'. These two stem-like parts,
quite easy to identify in the majority of growing shoots,
end by combining to form one single axial piece which is
the true stem of the plant. When the root consists of a
distinct cylindrical body, the stem and the root are the
axis of the organism. The disc of tissue which unites one
with the other is called the 'root collar'. We shall study
each of these parts separately.

THE STEM. The stem is that part of the plant's axis which
grows and rises up above the ground; it has an apical bud
and leaves along its sides. It may branch in several ways or
it may remain quite simple. When young it has a green
colour because the external cells contain chlorophyll.
There are also plants with underground stems, and these
are not green nor do they have normal leaves. These are

the rhizomes, fleshy and bulbous, but we shall deal with them separately at a later stage.

At the very tip of the apical bud we have the 'growing point', conical and diminutive, and the arbiter of all that concerns the organization of the plant over which it presides. On its sides are formed several protuberances which grow very rapidly and become more marked and prominent as they get left behind by the growing point. They are the 'leaf primordia' and soon surpass in height the growing point itself; the whole is called the 'apical bud'. The leaf primordium, by reason of its unequal growth, which is greater on its underside than its upper, has a tendency to curve upwards and inwards, thus protecting the growing point.

As the generator of the plant's structure, the growing point is of the greatest importance to it. In the higher plants it is composed of a group of cells endowed with enormous generative activity and capable of producing new cells predestined to form particular cellular tissues. Thus, all the epidermal cells of the plant originate from the external cellular stratum of the growing point; and the leaves come from those protuberances which arise on its sides and from the cellular strata immediately below the cells which generate the epidermis. In contrast, the growing point of the majority of ferns has but a single triangular cell with its base slightly convex and facing upwards; the growing point is thus so small that it might almost be given the geometrical definition of having position but no magnitude. It is, however, every bit as efficient as that of a flowering plant because that triangular pyramidal cell is producing new cells from each of its three sides, and these cells are separated by membranes which are parallel to each of the lateral faces of the tetrahedron.

DEVELOPMENT OF THE STEM. When a growing point is examined, it is soon seen that the leaf primordia separate from each other as they develop, the upper from the lower. As they become changed into leaves there is always some distance between each leaf and the next, or between the pairs of leaves if they grow opposite each other. The points along the stem where leaves have formed from the primordial leaves are called 'nodes' because in the majority of plants the stem thickens noticeably at these points. In the stem of a carnation, for example, which has opposite leaves, the nodes are immediately obvious. The portions of stem between the nodes are called 'internodes'.

If we separate the leaf primordia and the incipient leaves from the stem, we see that the latter develops close to the growing point and elongates rapidly. As we shall see later, there exists in the stem a zone of apical growth sometimes of considerable extent.

LOCATION OF THE LEAVES. From what we have said, it is evident that leaves do not spring from random points along the stem but from nodes which are determined at the growing point and develop in a regular manner as they are formed. The rest of the stem has no capacity for growing leaves.

There are plants which have a single leaf at each node so that in the mature stem the leaves are 'alternate', although at first sight they may seem to be arranged haphazardly. Other plants have two leaves at each node, one facing the other, and are said to be 'opposite' (decussate), while those with three or more per node are called 'whorled' (verticillate). The grouped leaves around a node may thus constitute a 'whorl'. See Fig. 6.

It is now more than four centuries since Leonardo da Vinci, in his *Trattato della Pittura*, said: "Nature has arranged the leaves on the branches of many plants in such a way that the sixth leaf is always situated directly above the first—and the seventh above the second, etc.—unless this should be interupted in some way." The famous painter's observation was the first in a series of studies related to the arrangement of leaves along the stem, and a study of this kind is called 'phyllotaxonomy' or 'phyllotaxis'. It has since been found that the order discovered by

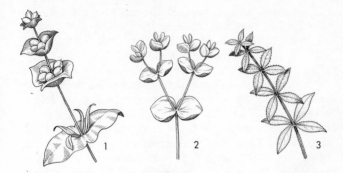

Fig. 6

Opposing leaves. 1, Honeysuckle. 2, Spurge (*Euphorbia*). 3, Verticillate leaves of madder (*Rubia peregrina*). Reduced.

Leonardo is actually quite common, but it is by no means the only one, nor the simplest.

When leaves spring from both sides of the stem and lie in the same plane, but alternate from right to left with but one leaf at each node, we can see that if a lower leaf were to be removed and placed in the position of the next leaf up the stem, the transposition would trace a spiral path round the stem for one half turn. In other words, two consecutive leaves on the stem would be separated by an angle of 180 degrees, and this is referred to as the 'angle of divergence' of the leaves. This angle is always measured by taking a medial section through the axis of the stem and the midrib or principal vein of the leaf or leaves concerned. In the case just cited the angle of divergence is equal to a half-circle.

There are other species of plants which have successive leaves separated by one-third of a circle, that is by 120 degrees. Here, following a spiral round the stem, as we did before, we find that we need only go a third of the way round before coming across the next leaf. In the case studied by Leonardo da Vinci it would be necessary to make two complete turns of the stem before reaching the sixth leaf. Put in another way, if we make two turns we encounter five leaves, because the angle of divergence is now equal to two-fifths of a circle.

There are also more complicated leaf arrangements, which, if we start with the angles of divergence 1/2 and 1/3 of a circle, can be expressed by a series of fractions in which the numerators and denominators are made of the sums of the numerators and denominators of the preceding two fractions, thus: 1/2, 1/3, 2/5, 3/8, 5/13, 8/21 . . . The last happens to be the angle of divergence of the scales on the cones of *Picea excelsa* (spruce).

Looking at the stem from below in the direction of its axis, we see that when the angle equals 1/2 circle the leaves are arranged in two rows, and when it is 2/5, in five rows, and so on. These ideal lines passing through the points of insertion of the leaves are called 'orthostics'. The number of orthostics is the same as the denominator of the fraction describing the angle of divergence, and is easily seen in the earlier members of the series, but as we pass to divergences greater than 2/5 its determination becomes more difficult.

It is usual to construct a 'diagram' of the leaf arrangement by drawing the spiral on paper as viewed from above. We thus get a sort of 'catherine wheel' with the outermost turn representing the base of the stem and the centre representing the growing point. The points of insertion of the leaves are then plotted. When we are dealing with opposite and whorled leaf arrangements, instead of the spiral we use a series of concentric circles with the same number of circles as there are nodes, and then we plot the positions of the leaves on each circle.

These ways of showing arrangements of leaves on stems and branches are of considerable importance since they are also applied to flowers. We look upon the latter as short stems or buds having petals instead of leaves, sometimes verticillate but sometimes following a spiral line.

LEAVES. When the primordial leaves have completed their development they emerge as true leaves. In most cases leaves are laminate, green, have a surface (or upper face) and an underside, and are of a definite shape. For each species the dimensions are constant within certain limits. The sizes of the leaves need have no relation to the size of the trunk or stem; there are very big trees with small leaves, such as the sequoia, and small plants with very large leaves like the Victoria regia water-lily and some palm trees and tree-ferns. While the stems and trunks seem to be capable of indefinite upward and outward growth—some of the larger trees reaching over 300 feet in height—the leaves have more limited expansion (with the exception of *Welwitschia mirabilis*).

A normal leaf when it reaches full maturity is composed of three parts: the 'petiole' or leaf stalk, which grows out of the node and supports the leaf, the 'blade' or 'lamina', which is the flat part of the leaf and can be called the leaf proper, and lastly, at the base of the petiole there often is a widened part where it is attached to the stem, and frequently encircling it, called the 'sheath'. When the leaf has no petiole and the blade is inserted directly into the stem, it is called 'sessile'; when it has a stalk, it is 'petiolate'. When the sheath is very well developed and embraces a good stretch of stem, as in the grasses, we talk about 'sheathing leaf bases'. At the junction of the petiole with the stem we occasionally see two appendices, laminar or otherwise and usually small, which are the 'stipules'.

Fig. 7

Leaf of bean plant, with two large stipules at the base, two pairs of unequal folioles (leaflets), and a ramifying tendril at the tip. (*After* Baillon).

B*

Practically all the Leguminosae possess them and they are very conspicuous on bean and pea plants (see Fig. 7).

In many leaves, the petiole seems to extend itself right through the blade from the base to the apex or tip, like a vein; this is the 'midrib' of the leaf. In a typical leaf, 'secondary veins' branch out from the midrib on either side of it, like the vanes of a quill. In other leaves, veins of equal importance with the midrib branch out from the base of the latter and diverge on either side very much like the fingers of an open hand. The first of these types of leaf is 'pinnately veined', and the second 'palmately veined'. More rarely, veins resembling this second class run through the blade in parallel lines from the base to the tip; this is 'parallel veining'.

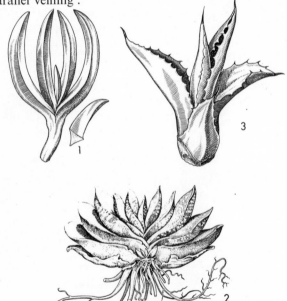

Fig. 8

Fleshy leaves. 1, Trigonal leaves (*Carpobrotus edulis*). 2, 'Distichous' leaves—i.e., leaves arranged in two opposite lines (*Gasteria*). 3, Leaves with spiny edges (aloe). Reduced.

SHAPES OF LEAVES. The shape of the leaf-blade varies enormously, but, except in leaf primordia or on very young plants, the blade usually acquires a definite form which is typical for each species of plant. The blade is sometimes thick and fleshy, and may be triangular or 'trigonal' in section (Fig. 8).

Leaf shapes are frequently described in terms of geometrical figures, so that we say they are round, oblong, oval, elliptical, triangular, etc. Or again, we may compare them to well-known objects and say that they are ovate (egg-shaped), lanceolate (shaped like a lance), heart-shaped, reniform (kidney-shaped), etc., terms which really need little explanation.

FORM OF THE LEAF BLADE. Soon after its formation, the leaf primordium frequently undergoes a change in shape; on each of its sides, well-defined prominences are seen to develop. As the leaf grows, these prominences may become more and more evident, though in some cases they grow so little that they may be hardly noticeable. Thus, the leaf does not become adult without achieving some sort of division into segments or lobes, often quite pronounced, or at least showing small marginal indentations which are sometimes almost imperceptible. We can see, therefore, that if we want to complete our studies of the morphology of the leaf, we must pay some attention to its edges.

Leaves which do not have indentations but have smooth, straight edges are said to be 'whole' or 'entire'. When the modification ceases in its initial stages and the leaf border shows no more than a series of notches, we say the leaf is 'dentate'; while if the notches are sharp and quite pronounced, it is 'serrated'. There are cases in which shallow undulations occur at the edges, and these are fairly long in the 'sinuated' leaves, but shorter and more regular in the 'festooned' leaves. As the indentations along the margins increase in depth, the leaves are given different names according to the type of veining and the way in which the clefts or 'sinuses' are arranged. The first part of

Fig. 9
Leaves with palmate veining. Palmatipartite leaves of 1, common fig (*Ficus*); 2, buttercup (*Ranunculus*); 3, ivy-leaved toadflax (*Linaria*); 4, maravilla (*Pharbitis*).

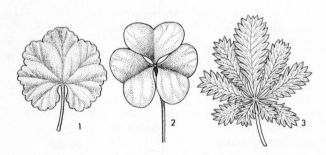

Fig. 10
Leaves with palmate veining. 1, Palmatilobulate (*Pelargonium*). 2, Trifoliate (*Oxalis*). 3, Palmatisect (*Potentilla*).

the name given has to do with the veining and may begin 'pinnati-' or 'palmati-' according to whether the leaf is pinnate or palmate; the suffixes are three; '-fid' is used if the sinus does not reach the middle of the half-leaf, '-partite' if it passes the middle yet does not reach the midrib, and '-sect' when the sinus actually meets the midrib or the base of the lamina. Thus we may have: 'pinnatifid', 'pinnatipartite' and 'pinnatisect' leaves; and again, 'palmatifid', 'palmatipartite' and 'palmatisect' leaves. See Figs. 9 and 10.

It is, however, by no means rare for the lobes of leaves to be themselves ramified and have dentate, sinuate, lobulate or segmented margins. Thus we see leaves that are 'bipinnatipartite', 'bipinnatifid' and 'bipinnatisect'. This process may be extended further to give 'tripinnatifid' leaves, etc. A selection of interesting leaf forms is given in Figs. 11 and 12.

COMPOUND LEAVES. When the unscientific writer tells us that he took his afternoon nap "beneath the shade of the carob tree (St. John's Bread), the 'lenticular' (lentil-shaped) leaves of which give such agreeable shade during the hot summer afternoons", we must confess that he is not being strictly accurate. However, we must be lenient with him because he does not claim to be giving a scientific description, just as we must be tolerant of the individual who says that of all the fish in the sea, he likes the lobster best. When the study of natural history began to take on scientific exactness and expression, it was found that the everyday terms used to describe most things were helpful in some cases but definitely hindrances in others. Today, in the eyes of scientific persons, it would be an unforgivable sin to say that the lobster was a fish, or that the carob tree had lentil-shaped leaves. Lobsters are crustaceans and carob tree 'leaves' are leaflets—parts of compound leaves, like those of the ash, acacia and rose.

When the segments of a segmented leaf assume an individuality of their own, and adopt similar shapes and

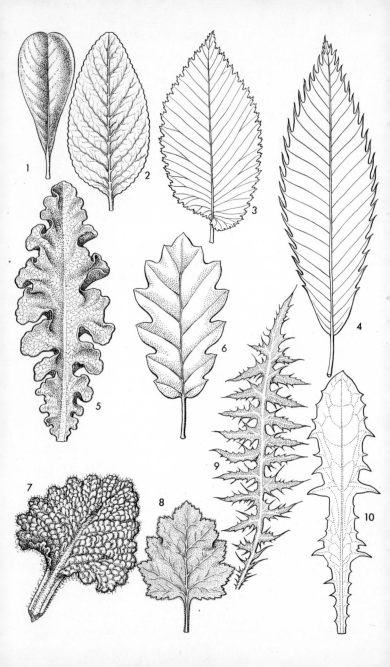

sizes or very nearly so, and even have their own little stalks, then we say that the leaf is a 'compound' one, and each one of its individual segments is called a leaflet (Fig. 12–8). The true leaves of the carob tree (or of the rose) have a 'rachis', which is an extension of the petiole into a long slender structure corresponding to the midrib of an ordinary leaf. Into this rachis are inserted a number of leaflets on each side, which are the so-called lentil-shaped leaves. The rachis of the bean leaf in Fig. 7 terminates in a branching tendril.

The compound leaves which have pinnate veining are called 'pinnately compound'; their leaflets are disposed in pairs in two rows, one on either side of the rachis. In such cases it can happen that there is a final leaflet at the very tip, so we say that the leaf is made up of *n* pairs of leaflets plus one odd one at the apex; we then say it is 'pinnate with an odd leaflet', or 'imparipinnate'; when this terminal leaflet is missing we say that the leaf is 'paripinnate'. There are also compound leaves with palmate veining; they are called 'palmately compound'. In many leguminous plants, the leaflets themselves are branched and produce secondary leaflets; in this case they are called 'bipinnately compound', and we might add that there are others even more complex.

HETEROPHYLLY. There are cases where the leaves on the young shoot or plant are quite different from those on the fully grown plant; this phenomenon is called 'heterophylly' and is relatively common, but the young leaves must be distinguished from the embryonic leaves or cotyledons, which are almost always distinct from normal leaves.

Fig. 11

Kinds of leaves. 1, Inverted ovate or 'obovate' leaf, slender at the base and (in this case) with smooth or 'perfect' edges. 2, Ovate and dentate. 3, Double-dentate and asymmetrical (elm). 4, Lanceolate and deeply-indented (sweet chestnut). 5, Pinnatipartite with wavy lobes (*Verbascum sinuatum*). 6, Pinnatifid (oak). 7, Deltoid, sinuate and embossed (borage). 8, Lobulate with indented lobules. 9, Pinnatisect and spiny (*Galactites tomentosa*). 10, Unequal lobulo-dentate.

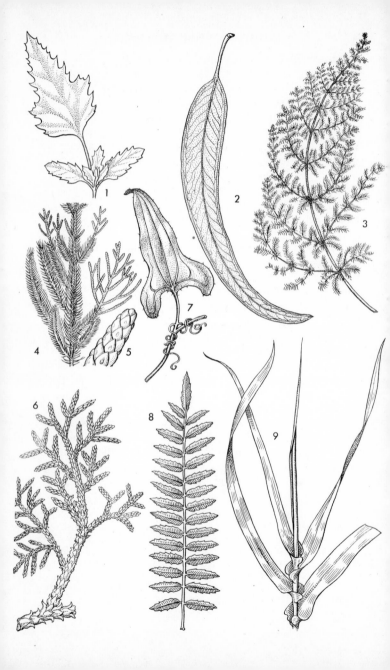

Heterophylly can be seen quite well in the common hare-bell. The leaves of the young harebell are round or kidney-shaped and have long petioles or stalks, whereas those of the mature plant are narrow or lanceolate and either have very short petioles or are sessile.

In general, where heterophylly exists, the lower leaves situated between the cotyledons and the adult leaves are called 'cataphylls'. But sometimes, between the adult or 'normal' leaves the flowers of the plant, other leaves are seen, often quite distinct from the normal ones, and these, because they are situated high up on the plant, have been given the name of 'hypsophylls'. Flowers themselves are none other than modified leaves, and the closer the petals are to the centre of the flower the more modified they become. Floral leaves or petals are called 'antophylls'. Fundamentally, all the mentioned types of leaves are composed of laminar appendages springing from the axis of the stem, and they are given the general name of 'phyl-lomes'. The complete series of leaves of a heterophyllic plant is, then: cotyledons, cataphylls, normal leaves, hypsophylls and antophylls.

THE LIFE OF THE LEAF. As a rule, cotyledons have a short life, but there are exceptions in such unusual plants as *Welwitschia mirabilis*. In the annuals, so-called because they only live for a year, the leaves die one after the other until they are all gone, and the whole plant withers and dies within twelve months after it sprouted. In the peren-nial plants, the leaves may last more or less longer than a year and they fall from the stems and branches in a num-

Fig. 12

More kinds of leaves. 1, Pinnatifid (chenopod). 2, Falciform (eucalyptus). 3, Tripinnatisect (*Meum athamanticum*). 4, Shoot showing foliar dimor-phism—that is to say, having two kinds of leaves, some needle-like and others squamous or scale-like (*Juniperus phoenicea*). 5, Tip of a small branch of the previous shoot, magnified to show the scale-like leaves. 6, Small branch of cypress showing similar leaves. 7, Leaf of sarsaparilla showing spiny edges. 8, Compound leaf, imparipinnate with dentated folioles (*Schinus molle*). 9, Leaves with parallel veining (common cane).

ber of ways. In the deciduous trees and shrubs, all the leaves are shed and the branches may remain without foliage for some time.

The fall of the leaves generally happens at the beginning of a period which is unfavourable for the growth of the plant. Such periods may have several causes. For example, as winter approaches the shortened days mean less sunlight; or the cold weather may bring with it frosts which prevent the plant's absorbing water and maintaining its hydraulic equilibrium; again, there may be a prolonged drought. Plants which lose all their leaves on such occasions are called 'deciduous', and those which retain leaves all the year round are called 'evergreen'. In the evergreens the leaves may last for more than a year and they are replaced in such a way that the tree always has green foliage and is well supplied with leaves.

BRANCHING OF STEMS. Some plants have stems which commence branching quite early in the plant's life, dividing to form smaller branches in various ways. This branching is most noticeable in the trees and is the main cause of their characteristic outlines. For instance, there are great differences between the shapes of such trees as the spruce and the araucaria, on the one hand, and the apple and the plane tree on the other.

On a simple stem without branchings we see that the leaves are arranged in such a way that only rarely does one leaf get in the way of another, so that the function of photosynthesis is impeded as little as possible. When the plant grows and eventually branches, the limbs develop so as to display their leaves in the most efficient way possible, thus ensuring the maximum leaf-surface exposed to sunlight. The ways in which plants branch, although extremely varied as to detail, fall into three fundamental types: 'dichotomous', 'monopodial' and 'sympodial'.

'Dichotomous branching' is quite rare among the higher plants and occurs because the terminal cell or group of cells at the growing point divides into two. The result is two

branches of equal importance, each one of which now
functions independently as an apical cell and divides again,
the plant continuing its development by means of this successive forking. This type of branching is seen to advantage
in the club-mosses *Selaginella* and *Lycopodium*.

In contrast to this special type of 'terminal branching',
where division takes place at the growing point, the most
common branching takes place along the sides of the stem
or trunk, or of a previously formed branch. This type is
called 'lateral branching'. Here, the axis or stem continues
its upward growth indefinitely for the rest of its life, and
the growing point maintains its activity. The plant depends
both upon the apical bud and the side shoots, which grow
from the main stem to give it the form characteristic of its
species. The growing point may be continuously active, or
it may have periods of rest or reduced activity, after which
it will recover its powers of growth as its environment
approaches optimum conditions again. It is in this way
that the spruce and the fir grow, their pointed tops remind-
ing us of the shape of a Gothic arch. In trees, this type of
branching means that the trunk has preference over the
branches. The trunk is a single unit and constitutes what
we call a 'monopodium'; that is to say, the axis forms a
single part by reason of the way the plant grows.

The kind of branching called monopodial, just described, is characteristic of the conifers, but there is another
type which is far more common and of which we can find
any number of examples. The apple and plane trees, to
which we have already referred, branch at first mono-
podially, but this lasts for only a limited period of their
growth. In fact, when they are young, they have a simple
or branched stem, quite erect and with the apical growing
point at its most active and obviously taking precedence
over any side shoot activity. But the time comes, usually at
the beginning of a period of adverse conditions for the
organism, when the apical growing point begins to lose its
vigour and its activity slows until it stops altogether. Then,
when the plant recovers and starts to grow again the ter-

minal bud remains totally inoperative, being now quite
incapable of further growth, and development takes place
at the nearest lateral bud. This now sends out a branch
following approximately the same direction as the apical
bud on the stem did before.

Since this process is repeated each time that the trunk
experiences a period of rapid growth, we can see that the
result will be a tree apparently composed of several portions joined together, rather than of a straight stem as in
the fir or spruce. The trunk is naturally of the same substance throughout, but as it has been produced from a
series of distinct buds it is therefore 'heterogeneous'.
Instead of a monopodium, we now have what is called a
'sympodium', and the type of branching is 'sympodial'.

INFLORESCENCES. The two kinds of branching, monopodial and sympodial, may be studied quite easily in
umbels or flower clusters (called 'inflorescences') because
here the whole procedure of ramification is often run
through within a few weeks. The many kinds of inflorescence result from indefinite or definite prolongations of
the stem, and, in the first case, from the relative lengths of
the axis and the branches which sping from it, as well as
from the distances between internodes.

Monopodial branching is represented by the type of
inflorescence called 'racemose' (from the Latin *racemus*,
a bunch of grapes). Strictly speaking, the raceme consists
of a simple axis growing from its apex to indefinite size,
almost exactly like a spruce or fir in miniature, with the
apical bud always active and sending out side shoots all
round the stem as it grows. However, in the raceme the
branches are the stalks or 'peduncles' which bear flowers
at their tips. The lower flowers are the first to form and
open, and naturally the latest ones to appear will be those
at the apex of the stem, which are the most newly formed.
The stalks or peduncles supporting the flowers, once they
have fully developed, are all of equal length, as also are
the distances between the stalks if measured along the

stem from their points of insertion. The raceme may be formed in a variety of ways and arrangements, and the following paragraphs should be read with reference to Fig. 13.

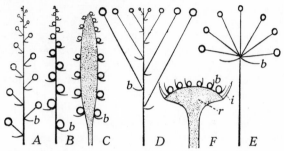

Fig. 13

Racemose inflorescences. *A*, Raceme. *B*, Spike. *C*, Spadix. *D*, Corymb. *E*, Umbel. *F*, Head. *b*, bract; *i*, involucre; *r*, receptacle.

If the peduncles supporting the flowers become so short that the latter are virtually inserted directly into the stem, then the inflorescence is not a raceme but a 'spike'. Do not, however, think of an ear of wheat as an example of this type of inflorescence, because wheat really has a compound inflorescence and would be better called a 'spike of spikes'. The best example is the common plantain, found in Europe and America. Sometimes there is a spike of unisexual flowers, male and female, arranged around a fleshy axis in all sorts of ways; in such a case the inflorescence is given the name of 'spadix', and examples are afforded by the arum lily and cuckoo-pint. But it often happens that the peduncles are unequal; that is to say, that some flowers are supported by long stalks and others by short ones. Usually, when this occurs, we find that the long peduncles are those at the base of the inflorescence, and they become shorter towards the apex until they are practically non-existent at the very tip. In such cases, the raceme does not lengthen indefinitely but adopts a conical shape, point downwards and flat or almost so at the top.

The Cruciferae of the genus *Iberis*, (the candytuft), have this kind of inflorescence, which is called a 'corymb'. We find that the cabbages, radishes, mustards and in fact almost all the rest of the Cruciferae, form racemes.

Now, then, let us suppose that in a corymb the distances which separate the points of origin of the peduncles are reduced to zero; that is to say, that we are given an example in which they all leave the stem at the same point and are all of the same length. In this case, with all the peduncles arranged radially, we have a floral cluster whose flowers form a rounded surface; they will lie on a part of a sphere. This kind of florescence is called an 'umbel', and ivy affords a good example.

All types of inflorescence derived from the raceme, that is, the monopodia, are called 'racemose inflorescences', and most extraordinary examples may be found in the so-called 'heads' of the large group of compound racemose inflorescences. We consider the head to have been derived originally from an umbel, in which the peduncles were reduced almost to nothing and flattened so that the flowers seem to be attached to a single common peduncle and inserted directly into it. Rarely, the heads are spherical, for instance in the genus *Echinops*; usually, however, the flowers are inserted into the apical dilated portion of the common peduncle, called the 'receptacle'—flattened as in the sunflower, convex as in the dandelion, conical as in the common chamomile, and so on.

Because, as a rule, the peduncles of racemose inflorescences arise in the axils of the hypsophylls or 'bracts', it follows that in umbels as well as heads all the bracts must be arranged in a circle at the same level at the base of the umbel or around the receptacle of the head; this circle of bracts is known as the 'involucre'. Before the head opens, the involucre protects the small flowers it contains, forming a sort of floral bud.

As we have just seen, the racemose inflorescences, because of the way they branch (so clearly shown in the raceme), are monopodial. The inflorescences of the sym-

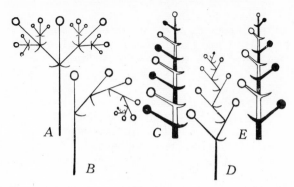

Fig. 14

Cymose inflorescences. *A*, Biparous cyme. *B*, Uniparous cyme: drepanium. *C*, The same straightened and showing the axes, bracts and shoots. *D*, Uniparous cyme: rhipidium. *E*, The same, straightened.

podial type are called 'cymes' or 'cymose inflorescences' (see Fig. 14). The growing point of a tree of the sympodial type, as we have mentioned, ceases its development at a certain stage and the main axis 'hands over' its duties to a lateral bud which then takes on the job of upward growth. In inflorescences of this type, the apical bud either produces a flower or it atrophies, and we may observe this taking place soon after inflorescence has started. If it atrophies, then one, two or several buds immediately below it carry on with the development of the floral cluster. In this way cymes are produced.

A common type is the 'biparous cyme', which, terminating in a flower on the main stem, has various lateral side shoots on either side, each branching into two stalks and bearing a flower in the fork of the bifurcation. Each of these stalks then bifurcates in its turn and once more flowers are formed in the fork, and so on indefinitely. When the first lateral branch ramifies, we often find that the branches of the second group are so unequal that there is virtually only one branch below the apical flower of the second group, and so on with the third and fourth groups, etc. It often happens that when a plant behaves like this it seems to lack the vigour to proceed with the double branching after the first ramification; in other words, when the apical bud has found its flower, no more than one lateral bud grows out to give more. So, instead of biparous we have 'uniparous cymes'.

When all the lateral branches of the uniparous cyme are found in the same plane, that is, the plane determined by the stem axis and the first branching, two cases may be presented. First, all the lateral branches may spring from the same side of the stem as the first one; second, they may appear alternately on the left and right of the stem (but also on the same plane). The first type is called a 'drepanium', and the second a 'rhipidium'. If the branches of the uniparous cyme are not all in the same plane, they still may tend to occur on one side or to fall on alternate sides. In the first case we have a 'cincinnus', quite common in the Boraginaceae, and in the second a 'bostryx', which is a curled rhipidium since it tends to develop spirally.

Sometimes, the lateral branch of the uniparous cyme, or its lower part, raises itself up in the same direction as the principal axis which produced it, and the peduncles of the successive floral buds are set to one side. In such cases, both the drepanium, and the rhipidium seem to have been formed from a single continuous axis, with all the flowers either to one side or disposed alternately on both sides. Only by careful study of this type of inflorescence can one discover its true nature, because it could so easily be confused with a raceme.

Finally, it can happen that the branches of a cyme number far more than one or two, and in such cases three or more lateral branches are formed below the terminal flower of the principal axis, and we have a 'pleochasium'.

Fig. 15

Racemose inflorescences. 1, Raceme (pokeberry, *Phytolacca decandra*). 2, Raceme of umbels (ivy, *Hedera helix*). 3, Head (*Inula viscosa*). 4, Raceme (*Veronica salicifolia*). 5, Panicle of heads (*Prenanthes purpurea*). 6, Head of unifloral heads (globe thistle, *Echinops ritro*).

Pleochasia occur frequently in the spurges, well-known plants of the genus *Euphorbia*.

COMPOUND INFLORESCENCES. All the inflorescences we have described so far are simple ones; but there are also 'compound' inflorescences, some of which are illustrated in Fig. 15. If, on a raceme, several of the stalks themselves ramify, then we have a 'raceme of racemes'; that is, a 'panicle'. The *racemus*, or bunch of grapes, is a panicle. The Umbelliferae rarely form simple umbels; usually, each one of the stalks of an umbel branches to form a secondary umbel, so that a compound umbel—an 'umbel of umbels' —results. See Fig. 16. Second order umbels are called 'umbellules' and at their bases are the small circle of bracts

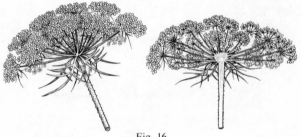

Fig. 16

Left: An umbel of umbels, or compound umbel, with its involucre at the base (*Daucus carota*). *Right*: The same in section, showing the dilation at the end of the peduncle.

or involucels. Compound inflorescences are not always derived from inflorescences of the same type; ivy, for example, bears racemes of umbels. On plants which have compound flowerings we can find racemes, corymbs, spikes, etc., and even panicles of heads. In the grasses, simple spikes are rare and they commonly form compound inflorescences, the branches of the axes being secondary spikes or 'spicules'.

In the same way, there are compound inflorescences in which we see both the racemose and the cymose types represented; these have been given the name of 'mixed inflorescences'. In the family of the Labiatae, for instance, large racemes are usually produced which do not just bear flowers, but more or less condensed cymes of flowers. See also the example illustrated in Fig. 17.

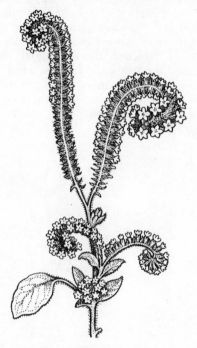

Fig. 17
Scorpioid cyme
(*Heliotropium europaeum*)

HOW BRANCHES ORIGINATE. As a rule, the shape and form of the future branches are already determined by the growing point and by the way in which the small protuberances which constitute the primordial leaves are formed. In the phanerogams, or flowering plants, there is a small region endowed with generative faculties next to each primitive leaf prominence, usually placed above the junction of the latter with the stem. Sometimes these faculties are manifest so early that already, near the apical bud, the primordial leaves show the rudiments of what will later become a lateral branch. In other instances, the development is so delayed that it only makes its appearance when the leaf is already formed or quite advanced in its growth. The part of the stem situated immediately above the point where the leaf is attached, and forming an angle with the petiole, is called the 'leaf axil'. The bud which is formed in this place is called the 'axillary bed,' and the branch the 'axillary branch'. The leaf immediately below the bud is called the 'tectorial' leaf, owing to its role of protector of the bud. See Fig. 18.

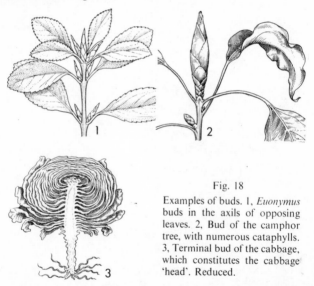

Fig. 18

Examples of buds. 1, *Euonymus* buds in the axils of opposing leaves. 2, Bud of the camphor tree, with numerous cataphylls. 3, Terminal bud of the cabbage, which constitutes the cabbage 'head'. Reduced.

There are cases where, once the formation of the axillary bud has started, but before it has developed into a branch or a flower, there is an outbreak of meristematic activity in the cauline or foliar tissue immediately beneath it. These cells, which have normally lost their generative powers, begin to divide and multiply until there a considerable amount of tissue is formed, with the result that the branch or the flower is raised up and away from the tectorial leaf. In these cases, the uninitiated might draw the conclusion that these were 'extra-axillary buds' because the branches or the flowers formed as a result of their activity do not appear to have been sent out exactly from the axil. This phenomenon is quite common in the Solanaceae.

The rapid development of apical buds in lilac is illustrated in Fig. 19.

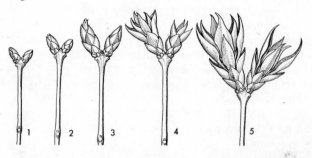

Fig. 19
Stages in the development of lilac buds, numbered in order.

ADVENTITIOUS BUDS. If we look upon the apical buds and the axillary buds as being quite normal because they can always be relied on to occur in their proper places, we must consider all buds which appear at random points on the plant as being 'adventitious'—that is to say, accidental. They are formed according to circumstances and in a seemingly casual manner. Thus, a begonia leaf, already adult and incapable of any further growth providing nothing happens to disturb its way of life, may acquire the faculty of providing adventitious buds if it is separated, together with the portion of stem belonging to it, from the parent plant and placed in damp soil under favourable conditions of temperature, etc.

THE ROOT. The axial part of the plant body which grows in the opposite direction to the stem and buries itself into the ground is called the 'root'. It acts as a support for the aerial part of the plant and provides it with water and dissolved salts which it absorbs from the earth. Because they are always buried and away from sunlight, the plastids of root cells are not converted into chloroplastids; in fact, the root is usually devoid of chlorophyll and, in contrast with the stem and leaves, does not have a green colour. However we must not assume that it is incapable of becoming green, for if any part of the root is uncovered and exposed to daylight it may quite easily turn green.

Roots do not bear leaves, nor do they bear any organ comparable with a leaf. When we see a root-like structure taken out of the ground bearing appendages very much like leaves, we know that this is not a root; it may be any of a number of stem-like organs which grow underground during some stage in the development of the plant body, and which we shall shortly describe. Since it has no leaves, the root therefore has no apical bud, nor indeed any buds of any kind.

The root takes its origin from the radicle of the embryo, with which we have already dealt (see page 35), and develops from a 'growing point' in which all the meristematic activity of the root is concentrated, but without buds or any protection of the sort which a bud usually has. We can thus see that, apart from the existence of a growing point (and not taking into account its internal structure), the root differs from the stem in a negative way by having no chlorophyll, no leaves, no buds and by growing in the reverse direction. However, among its positive characteristics we can number a calyptra and absorptive root hairs.

Just as the growing point of the stem has the protection of the young leaves which form the apical bud, so the growing point of the root, which is also its most delicate part, is protected by a special structure called the 'calyptra' (Greek, a veil) or 'root cap'. See Fig. 20. The root cap has been compared to a pot-lid, to a hood or bonnet, and to a thimble, but the object most like the calyptra, both in its shape, and in the role it plays, is the ferrule of a walking-stick, which is perfectly suited for protecting the end of the stick as it is dug into the ground. Just as apical bud of a stem is an adequate defence against inclement weather, so the root cap protects the delicate growing point against the hardness of the earth through which the root must pass, and opens a way for it. It will be understood, therefore,

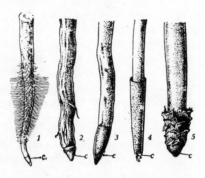

Fig. 20

Different aspects of root tips, showing the calyptra or root cap, *c.* 1, Idealised drawing in which the piliferous zone is also indicated. 2, *Asparagus officinalis.* 3, *Cattleya sp.* 4, *Lemna minor.* 5, *Pandanus sp.* (*Nos. 2 to 5 after* Bonnier).

that the calyptra is found at the very tip of the root, immediately on top of the growing point, and is like a small ivory-coloured callus with cells which harden rapidly but do not last indefinitely. The cap itself lasts, however, because although its cells are being constantly worn away they are continuously being replaced by others. The oldest cells are found at the tip of the root cap and are shed almost as soon as they arrive there, being replaced by the cells occupying the layer immediately below them; new cells are constantly being generated where the root cap is in contact with the growing point.

The 'root hairs' are found near the end of the root, but not quite at the very tip. They are formed in a similar way to the epidermal hairs—that is to say, by prolongation of the cells of the epidermis—but unlike the hairs on stems and leaves, which often grow quite thick with strong, robust membranes, the root hairs are extremely thin. Epidermal hairs die very soon, but they remain a part of the plant for a long time, not infrequently more than a year, or as long as the leaf lives; the life of the root hair, on the other hand, is ephemeral. Its job is to absorb water from the soil, which requires that its membrane be permeable, and this faculty is lost as the cell grows old. The younger hairs, that is to say the shortest, are those closest to the root tip; the older hairs—those farthest from the tip—become flaccid and lose their faculty of absorbing water, and they finish up by breaking away altogether from the root. The most active are the intermediate hairs and they are full and turgid.

As soon as a hair breaks away from the root, a cork-like cap is formed over the spot so as to make it waterproof. Absorption can no longer take place and the root tissues there concern themselves solely with the transportation of the fluids absorbed from other parts of the root, and of the vital sap. In addition to these functions the root system performs the very necessary office of anchoring the plant to the ground. It is clear, therefore, that to irrigate trees by scattering water at the base of the trunk is a waste of water and time in the majority of cases; the obvious thing to do is to water that area in which the ultimate ramifications of the root system are likely to be found—in other words, where the absorbing hairs lie. These often occur in the regions lying beneath the outermost new leaves of the tree.

VARIETIES AND SHAPES OF ROOTS. The main root of a plant is that which is formed from the radicle. At the beginning it resembles a nail driven into the soil, but it soon branches to a greater or less degree as it buries itself further down. When the branches are noticeably thinner and shorter than the main root, the dominance of the latter is assured for a considerable time if not indefinitely, and its axial character is clearly manifest. Such is called a 'tap root system' or 'primary root system', the tap root supporting the plant like a pile driven into the ground. Sometimes, instead of branching (except to give out thin and short rootlets) the tap root thickens considerably and becomes a sort of storehouse of reserve food for the plant. This type of root, because it is typical of turnips, is called 'napiform' (Latin *napus*, a turnip). In other cases, the branches or secondary roots grow to a fair size and lengthen, so that the main root loses its dominance and can no longer be called a tap root.

Roots which have not originated from the radicle are called 'adventitious roots'. Thus, if a cutting of carnation or geranium consisting of a piece of stem with a few leaves is planted in soil, under favourable conditions new roots are soon formed which are sent out from the stem; these are adventitious roots. Such roots are usually equal to one another in importance, length and thickness, and do not compete with each other. The same sort of thing happens when an onion is planted. From its base, which is a discoid stem, numerous rootlets of equal size are given out, and by reason of their bundle-like appearance they are said to be 'fascicular', the system being 'fasciculate'. When the main root dies off at an early stage, as for instance in the kidney bean, several adventitious fascicular roots arise from the hypocotyl. Fascicular roots are typical of the monocotyledons; that is, of all kinds of grasses, lilies, palms, etc. See Fig. 21.

Some adventitious roots have special names according to the part they play, or from their peculiar shapes. The ivy, for example, sends out small rootlets called 'adherent

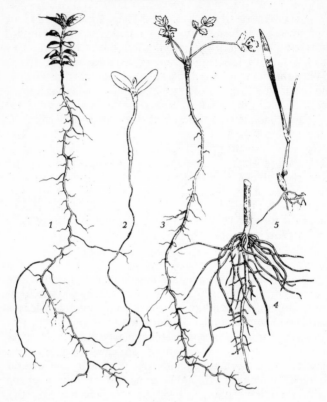

Fig. 21
Kinds of roots. 1, 2 and 3, Axonomorphic roots (*Viburnum tinus, Euphorbia sp.* and *Apium graveolens*, respectively). 4, Root with the axis not very well developed but showing several fasciculate adventitious roots (*Ricinus communis*). 5, Fasciculate root (barley).

roots' at the place where it is in contact with its support, and they have no other function than to enable the ivy to climb. In amny species of the Indian fig tree, roots spring from the branches and descend vertically to the ground, where they penetrate the surface and ramify. These are called 'fulcral roots', because they act as props for the branches, and when they are strong and very straight they may qualify for the name of 'columnar roots'.

Fig. 22
Left: Fulcral roots of *Pandanus*. *Right*: Adventitious roots of *Dracaena draco*, the 'dragon-tree' of the Canary Islands.

Other roots, like those of the mangrove tree, arise from the branches or from the trunk itself, and, arching outwards, dip down into adjacent water until they reach the silt or mud at the bottom, where they branch out and anchor themselves. There are also other types of fulcral roots which lift up the entire plant in the manner of stilts, as if they were determined that water should not reach the foliage. See Fig. 22.

4

Internal Structure of Vegetative Organs

THE STEM. When a woody stem has reached a certain stage in its development, and has matured, it may be seen to be composed of an external part called the 'cortex' and a central cylinder of wood, from which the cortex is easily separated. The wood, however, is not found near the growing point. The cortex itself is covered—as, indeed, is the whole plant—with the epidermis, a protective tissue with which we are already familiar. See Fig. 23. The cortex consists of parenchyma containing chloroplastids in its outer layers; when it is thick and inner layers remain colourless and lack chlorophyll. Generally, the peripheral parts of the cortex have strengthening structures of a collen-

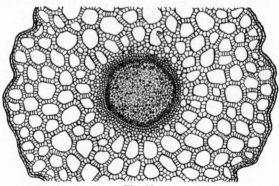

Fig. 23

Transverse section of the stem of an aquatic plant (*Hippuris*) showing the central cylinder. Between this and the epidermis is the cortical tissue, very well developed and containing many air chambers. (*From a photomicrograph by* Poilpot).

chymatous nature running longitudinally, which give more solidity and resistance to flexion. The innermost layer of cells, which is in contact with the central cylinder, is also devoid of chlorophyll and is often distinguished as the 'starch sheath' because it contains abundant starch deposits.

The most important components of the central cylinder are the 'vascular bundles'. As we have already seen, these are made up of strands containing elements capable of transporting fluid materials for considerable distances, such as vessels (tracheae and tracheids) and sieve tubes. The vascular bundles are surrounded by parenchyma which consolidates them and keeps them compact, and the outermost layer of the whole central cylinder—that which is in contact with the cortex—is called the 'pericycle'. The cells of the pericycle differ little, if at all, from those of the axial parenchyma, but they are very close together and they leave no intercellular spaces.

The number of bundles in the stem varies from plant to plant, but in general each stem has several forming an orderly ring around the plant axis. This region between the axis and the fascicular ring is filled with parenchyma, the cells of which have relatively short lives; they collectively form the 'medulla' or 'pith' and are sometimes reabsorbed by the plant leaving the stem hollow (Fig. 24). The radial strips of tissue which pass between the vascular bundles and which are really extensions of the pith, are called 'medullary rays' (Fig. 25). In the monocotyledons, such as the lilies and the palms, the vascular bundles are quite numerous and are disposed seemingly haphazardly though they are more abundant towards the stem periphery.

Vascular bundles raise the watery fluids absorbed from the soil by the roots to the top of the plant, and on their way they 'irrigate' the leaves according to their needs. This is possible because the vascular bundles send out branches or lateral strands to the leaves, which receive them through the petioles, and thence through the veins, until the entire leaf lamina has been afforded access to the

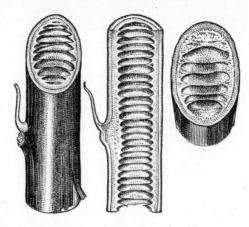

Fig. 24

Three portions of a stem of *Phytolacca decandra*, cut to show how the
medulla (pith) has been reabsorbed, leaving only equidistant discs of
very thin membrane. In several other plants the medulla disappears
entirely and the stem becomes a hollow tube (except at the nodes); this
occurs in some canes. Reduced.

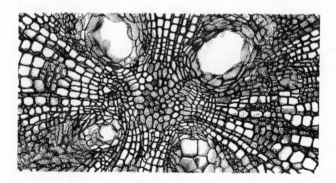

Fig. 25

Transverse section from the root of a pine tree, showing four resin-
bearing canals, the medulla in the centre, and numerous tracheids
disposed radially from the centre to the periphery, separated by medullary
rays. (*From a photomicrograph by* Poilpot).

contents of the bundles. Then the fluids return *via* a separate bundle of conducting elements and make their way to the stem where they follow a downward path.

If we examine carefully an isolated vascular bundle to see what elements it contains, we can soon distinguish vessels and sieve tubes arranged in a way that is typical of the species under observation. In the majority of flowering plants several vessels of varying size constitute the vascular part of the bundle; and various sieve tubes form the other part. That is to say, the two types of conducting tissue are quite separate, the vessels being found towards the centre and the sieve tubes on the outer part of the bundle. Since these bundles have the two types of element they are given the name of 'cribri-vascular bundles'. The sieve tubes form the 'bast', or inner bark—the soft innermost part of the cortex—and the vessels form the woody or ligneous part inside the central cylinder. Such bundles are called 'collateral bundles' when the vessels and the sieve tubes are placed side by side in their respective inner and outer zones. In the phanerogams, or higher plants, this is the most com-

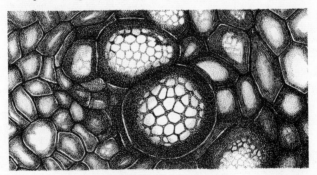

Fig. 26

Part of a transverse section of a melon stem, with sieve tubes in the centre. (*From a photomicrograph by* Poilpot).

mon arrangement, but there are, of course, numerous exceptions (see Fig. 26), and in other groups of plants there are other dispositions of the bundles. In a vascular bundle both the vessels and the sieve tubes are accompanied by specialised parenchyma cells, longer and narrower than those of the extrafascicular cauline parenchyma; in the sieve tube portion are found the so-called 'companion cells'. See Fig. 27 (1).

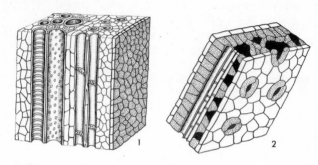

Fig. 27

The structure of stems and leaves, highly magnified. 1, Three-dimensional aspect of a piece of stem. The first layer on the right is the epidermis; next comes the cortex, in which are two sieve tubes separated by the so-called 'companion cells'; further to the left the cambium is represented by two cellular layers; then comes the conducting tissue, with one pitted vessel and one spiral-walled vessel, and finally parenchyma tissue. 2, Three-dimensional aspect of a piece of leaf. The first layer on the right is the epidermis of the under side of the leaf, with four stomata; one of these, on the edge, has been sectioned to show (in black) the air chamber. The first layer on the left is the epidermis of the upper surface of the leaf, and between the two layers of epidermis is the mesophyll. The part of the mesophyll beneath the upper epidermis consists of palisade parenchyma; below this is the conducting tissue of a leaf vein; between this and the lower epidermis lies the spongy parenchyma. (*After* Laubenfels).

STRUCTURE OF THE LEAF. When a leaf primordium has developed into an adult leaf, the internal differentiation of its tissues is just as perfectly definite as in the stem. To begin with, the leaf, like any other plant organ, is covered with and protected by the epidermis. When the epidermis is examined, it will be seen that in the great majority of cases the upper surface or face of the leaf is not identical with the lower surface or back; for example, the number of stomata is greater on the latter, and this fact shows that the two surfaces are as distinct microscopically as they are by simple naked-eye inspection.

The part of the leaf between the upper and lower layers of epidermis is the 'mesophyll'. Normally, the mesophyll is composed of one or more layers of elongated cells arranged perpendicularly to the leaf surface in such a way that, if the leaf is sliced in cross section and examined under the microscope, these cells appear to be set side by side, rather like the posts of a wooden fence; from this similarity has arisen their name of 'palisade parenchyma'. These parenchyma cells contain numerous chloroplastids, very well arranged in order to carry out the function of photosynthesis, because generally they are only separated from the exterior by the epidermis, which is translucent and acts as a sort of skylight on the upper surface of the leaf, this of course being the side receiving most light. See Fig. 27 (2).

The rest of the mesophyll is found underneath the palisade parenchyma and consists of 'spongy parenchyma', which is formed of cells of irregular shape, some larger than others; they are joined together in some way but leave numerous intercellular spaces of varying size. (See Fig. 28). Separated as they are from the upper surface by

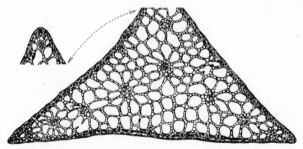

Fig. 28

Transverse section of a thick, triangular leaf of an aquatic plant (*Butomus*). The mesophyll is very well developed and contains large air passages and a number of sectioned veins. (*From a photomicrograph by* Laporte).

C*

the epidermis and the palisade parenchyma, they receive much less light than the latter and have less chloroplastids. But, all things considered, they contribute in no small way towards the photosynthetic functions of the plant. However, their most important duty consists in supplying air to the palisade parenchyma, since they provide passages between the stomata of the lower surface of the leaf and the layers of palisade cells. This spongy parenchyma is bounded underneath with the lower epidermis, which, as we have said before, is the side most richly endowed with stomata.

The bundles of sieve tubes and vessels which branch out from the stem and penetrate the leaf through its base, ramify throughout the lamina and constitute the vein system of the leaf. The central vein or midrib, and the smaller secondary, tertiary, etc. veins (which become smaller as they ramify), are composed of vascular bundles having the same structure and characteristics as those of the stem, though they become more and more simplified as they branch into the smaller veins. Bearing in mind that the vascular bundles have to arch out on their way from the stem into the leaves, we can readily deduce the positions in which the vessels and sieve tubes will be found. The vessels, the innermost components of the bundles as they run in the stem, ramify through the lamina along the upper part of the veins, while the sieve tubes (which occupy the outer part of the stem bundles) are to be found on the lower side of the vascular system as it runs through the leaf.

ROOT STRUCTURE. The newly formed root, while still young, is enveloped by the epidermis; its cells have very thin membranes and lack both cuticle and stomata. On the other hand, as we have seen above, several of these cells become considerably lengthened and form the 'absorptive hairs', which also have delicate membranes, and it is *via* these hairs that water and solutions of salts enter the root. The hairs are formed quite close to the root tip in the 'region of root hairs'; but further up the root, where the absorptive hairs (now flaccid and incapable of their job) fall away, the cellular layers on the surface of the root become impermeable by the formation of a protective cap of suberin; such layers are called the 'exodermis' instead of epidermis.

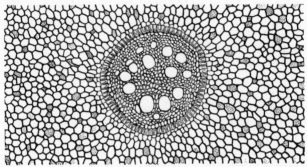

Fig. 29

Transverse section from the root of iris, showing the central cylinder surrounded by the cortical parenchyma. In the central cylinder the vascular bundles are seen in section, and surrounding them is the endodermis with its internal membranes and thickened lateral cells. (*From a photomicrograph by* Poilpot).

Beneath the exodermis (just as in the stem) the root consists of cortex and a central cylinder. The innermost layer of the former generally differs from the rest and is called the 'endodermis' (Fig. 29). In the root, as in the stem, we have the pericycle as the outermost part of the cylinder. To sum up, beginning from the outside we have first of all the exodermis, then the cortex proper and the endodermis; below the endodermis is the central cylinder containing the conducting elements, which, in the root, form a single group of bundles. In section, the components of the group are disposed radially; that is to say, there are several vascular bundles radiating from the centre, and between them are found formations of sieve tubes. See Fig. 26. The various units making up this single group of conducting elements conserve their arrangement while in the root, but when they get towards the stem, they regroup to conform to the particular pattern found in whatever species the stem may belong to.

SECONDARY GROWTH IN STEM AND ROOT. Until now we have been discussing the structures of root and stem as they appear when they have completed their development; that is, when the original cells which arose from the growing points of these organs have reached absolute maturity. This occurs in many cases some months after the germination of the seed, and if the plant in question happens to be one of the so-called annuals, then this is as far as it can develop and it dies away soon after. The plant flowers, produces its fruits and seeds, and then decays rapidly until there is nothing left. If, on the other hand, we are studying a perennial plant such as a tree, then the routine is quite different. The young plant does not flower but continues to grow for several years, and even when the time comes for it to produce flowers and fruits it does not perish but continues to grow and develop.

We have all seen how a tree grows, how its trunk lengthens and thickens, how it gives off its various branches and how the leaves are formed in such enormous quantities. Obviously, this considerable increase in mass cannot be due to the simple increase in volume of the cells which originated from the growing point of the young plant. Between the stem of the first shoot, a few inches high and a fraction of an inch thick, and the trunk of a grown tree, there is a vast dimensional difference. The cells which make up an ageing and majestic oak tree cannot possibly be the same cells, enlarged, which formed the young sapling, because if this were the case, each cell would need to increase in size several thousand times in order to make up the difference. This is, of course, biologically impossible, since the growth of a cell has fairly precise limits and is relatively small and constant for each species. Consequently, we must look for the source of the new cells which are evidently required for the formation of our imposing tree trunk and its ample foliage.

In the perennial spermatophyta, it is only the leaves which do not vary in size; the sapling and the adult tree both produce the same size of leaf, although there might even be a slight reduction in its dimensions as the tree gets very old. But the number of leaves increases so fantastically that, from a few dozen to begin with, there might be several hundred thousand in maturity. This applies to the great majority of trees, though there are some (like the palm-tree) which maintain a constant number all their lives.

Every tree, and in general, every plant, must base its economy of growth on what its leaves can produce and what its roots can absorb from the soil. Since each of these depends on the other, there must be a connection between the two to ensure co-ordination of supply and demand. The connection is found in the circulatory system of the plant—the conducting vessels which transport watery solutions from the soil, and the sieve tubes which carry more viscous substances, such as sap, from the tiniest vein on the highest leaf down to the lowest rootlet. Neither the trunk nor the root could continue to grow in size unless the conducting system constantly kept pace with their ever increasing needs. It is thus clear that it is the development of the conducting elements that determines to what size the plant body will grow.

In those plants which are destined to continue their development for many years we get that growth in thickness of stem called 'secondary growth'. At the growing points, things carry on as before and the meristematic tissues at such places are as active as ever. But in the stems and roots later thickening is achieved by means of the activity of certain rejuvenated cells, capable of multiplying. These are grouped to form another zone of tissue arranged cylindrically around the stem axis, its exact location being distinct for each species.

This generative zone is capable of producing two types of tissue; on one side, towards the interior of the trunk, conducting vessels are formed, and on the other side (towards the outside) sieve tubes are formed. Even from ancient times, long before it was recognised that it was a cellular zone, it was given the name of 'cambium' (from the Latin *cambire*, to exchange), and it was supposed to consist of a 'humour' which generated vessels and sieve tubes. The structure of the root and stem, as we have already described it, is altered by the work of the cambium, and we thus have primary growth followed by secondary growth. The 'primary tissues' are succeeded by other tissues, which are called 'secondary' because they proceed from the new generative zone and not from the growing points. At first, when the cambium has just started to operate, it is still possible to identify the primary and secondary structures in the stem and root, but later on, as the work of secondary tissue becomes more advanced, the primary structures gradually become obliterated, and in very old trees the great mass of cells which constitutes the trunks is wholly the product of the activity of the cambium.

THE WORK OF THE CAMBIUM: "WOOD" OR XYLEM. At the start of its activity this generative zone is placed not very far from the actual stem axis, because when the formation of new cells begins the shoot has only a very thin stem—no more than a few millimetres in diameter. As cells are produced on both sides, the vessels towards the centre, and the sieve tubes towards the outside, the internal cells necessarily surround the existing cells while the external ones are interposed between the cambium cells and the nearest layer of the outside cells. Let us therefore consider both types of tissue, the vessels and the sieve tubes, separately.

The vessels formed by the cambium are arranged in concentric circular layers, each layer being outside the previous one and therefore wider. In the same way that these rings of vessels continue to expand, so also does the cambium increase in diameter, since (relative to the vessel rings) it occupies an outside position. The number of its cells increases, too, for besides being capable of forming vessels and sieve tubes it can also produce more cambium cells. In a thick trunk, such a large number of vascular rings may have been formed that the cambium, situated at first only a few millimetres from the stem axis, may now be more than a yard from the centre.

We must not conclude that every vessel which forms the internal mass of the trunk is capable of transporting the aqueous solutions which ascend from the roots, because with time they lose their ability to transport liquids and become choked up or otherwise obliterated. The oldest vessels, that is to say the innermost ones, become converted into supporting elements and are very much toughened as their membranes lignify, while only the outside ones, those nearest to the cambium and consequently the youngest, are active. The former constitute the strongest wood of the trunk, which is called 'heart-wood' or 'duramen'; the vessels in full activity form an outer sheath, which is much softer and is called 'alburnum'. The needs of a tree while it is alive and growing become greater as time goes on because its branches and leaves increase in number. Thus, to satisfy these needs we can see that the circular zone of young vessels is admirably suited since it is correspondingly wider as the trunk increases its girth and therefore it must also be richer in conducting elements.

In countries which have a warm climate and a regular rainfall the cambium is active all the year round, with alternating periods of greater and less activity; but where there is a definite winter, or one or more periods of severe drought (unless the tree happens to be riparian, i.e., growing on a river bank), there is a marked periodicity in its activity. The slowing down of the tree's vital activities at the onset of autumn or a very dry season brings with it the gradual stoppage of the circulatory system. Thus it comes to a complete halt during the rigours of the winter or, in the other case, when the tree has completely exhausted the water reserves in the ground, and then the leaves are shed.

The activity of the cambium is also restricted somewhat

during these hard times, and the vessels which are formed become narrower and less numerous until finally they cease altogether. In those countries which have a very hard winter we have the spectacle of the impetuous bursting of the buds and the urgent growth of new leaves with the arrival of spring, and this calls for a renewal of the circulation in the plant in the full flow of its activity; but that which gradually came to a halt towards the end of the autumn does not equally slowly recuperate and regain its powers once the winter is over. On the contrary, we see a sudden awakening of the organism calling for the maximum output of its resources, because this is not just an effort to sustain life but a re-creation of the very tools of its trade—the countless leaves. Consequently, during this period of recovery the cambium produces vessels of large diameter all the time there is the need for them, but once the pressure is relaxed and the foliage is formed, they return to the smaller size just adequate for normal vital needs.

So, because the large vessels of increased diameter appear very rapidly and are laid alongside the autumnal vessels of much smaller calibre, the difference between these two vascular layers may be seen very clearly in a cross-section of a tree-trunk, where the lighter circular zones alternate quite regularly with the darker ones. If there should be one annual period of the slowing down of vital activity, for example as a consequence of low winter temperatures, then each one of these circles must correspond to a year in the life of the tree, and the total number of rings will be its age. For this reason we refer to them as 'annual growth rings'.

Naturally, in order that the tree thrive and prosper it is essential that, when water is required, the soil should hold sufficient to supply it. Although the annual xylem rings are formed regularly year after year, their width and substance may vary from a good year to a bad year. Interesting studies in climate have been made from examination of the annual growth rings in trunks of great age, and although conclusions drawn can only be approximate, it has been possible to make statements regarding the weather and climate in bygone ages from cross-sections of trees which have lived for hundreds of years.

STEMS OF PALM TREES AND FERNS. Those who have seen a palm tree develop from the nut will remember that at first the leaves form a kind of rosette at ground level. This rosette lasts for a number of years until, little by little, the plant grows upwards and the tuft of basal leaves gradually rises on a slender column. During its whole life, the palm tree retains the simplicity of a single axis, which branches very rarely indeed; it grows longitudinally only and does not widen, and the number of leaves are fairly constant across the years. It should therefore be noted that although trees of other species require more and more water as they increase in size and number of leaves, this is not the case with the palm tree. In fact, once the trunk has reached adult size it possesses sufficient conducting elements to last it for the rest of its life. The growing point, compared with those of other species, is very wide and from it arises the entire plant structure. The stem structure of the young tree, with its numerous vascular bundles, remains the same during the life of the plant. Ferns also have this type of stem, and so do the tree-ferns of many tropical and sub-tropical forests.

THE INNER BARK OR PHLOEM. In preceding paragraphs we have studied what happens on the inside of the cambium layer, and it now remains to see the changes which take place on the outside of this generative zone, which is so important to the development of the tree.

The cambium, when it engenders new tissue towards the exterior, changes its plan, so to speak; instead of making vessels or tracheids, it produces sieve tubes. These tubes are interposed between the cambium and the existing ring of sieve tubes belonging to the primary stem structure. Thus, just as the oldest vessels are found towards the centre of the trunk, so the oldest sieve tubes are found on the outside. The vessels continue to be superimposed on the previously formed ones because the cambium increases its own distance from the stem axis; the sieve tubes are deposited on the outside of the cambium and remain confined within the cortex.

The crushing of conducting elements, which takes place as layer after layer is deposited, is naturally felt most at the outside of the trunk. There are two commonly cultivated species, the plane tree and the eucalyptus, which annually give us unquestionable proof of this. Both trees behave like snakes—they shed their skins. The 'skin' of the plane tree peels off the trunk in the form of almost flat sheets, while that of the eucalyptus in long thin greyish strips, almost rolled up like tubes. In either case the new cortex lies beneath, and that which falls consists of portions of dead cortical matter, no longer of any value to the plant.

The process by which all this takes place is much more complicated than it seems at first sight, because new external cambiums are formed, producing impermeable cortical layers which eventually kill off all tissues lying external to them. But, simplifying the matter for easier understanding, the only solution left to the plant to get out of its difficulty and make room for the new cambium is to increase the diameter of the cortex, splitting it more or less deeply or otherwise breaking it when it offers resistance to the pressure beneath.

Everything which the cambium produces towards the exterior is called the 'phloem'. Unlike the wood or xylem its width is always limited. A tree with a thick trunk may have a great thickness of wood, but the thickness of the cortex always remains approximately the same. The mass of dead tissue which surrounds it, together with the scales, sheets and long narrow strips which peel off it, are collectively called the 'rhytidoma'.

SECONDARY GROWTH IN ROOTS. In the monocotyledons, the true root atrophies very soon and is replaced by a bunch of adventitious roots of the same kind. This is the case, for instance, in the roots of the palm, maize, onion, etc., all of which soon reach their maximum thickness and lack secondary growth in this direction.

But this does not hold for the great majority of trees and shrubs, whether they be gymnosperms or dicotyledons. There is all the difference in the world between the root of a sapling and that of a fully grown tree, when it comes to length and thickness. The root of a large tree not only has to attend to its mechanical duties, such as anchoring the tree in the ground, but it has to see to all fluid requirements and supply such water as may be needed. As is the case with the stems, the roots of such trees develop quite considerably as a result of the activity of the cambium.

We have already seen how the primary structure of a root differs from the primary structure of a stem, in that the root has radially arranged bundles consisting of groups of vessels with groups of sieve tubes between them. The result is that, in roots, the generative zone which constitutes the cambium has a sort of zig-zag outline in cross-section, because it originates between the phloem and the root axis but at the same time it must pass outside the xylem or groups of vessels. However, before long this sinuosity disappears and the cambium becomes quite circular. Just as in the stem, the cambium forms woody vessels towards the inside and sieve tubes externally, so in an old root the central part consists of a compact woody mass, and around this lies the cortex with its most recently grown and active part facing inwards.

5

Modifications of the Plant Body

METAMORPHOSIS. Taking as our standard of normality the plant body with a long branching stem, laminar leaves and a tap-root, or branched or fascicular roots, let us regard any plant that is in some definite way different as having been evolved by 'metamorphosis'. This concept assumes a protomorphosis or primary morphosis—that is to say, a first formation under normal biological conditions of a vegetable type possessing the above-mentioned characteristics throughout the species. Then we suppose a series of subsequent modifications (secured through heredity) which adapt the species to altered or abnormal biological conditions.

Owing to the changes wrought by metamorphosis, a stem may appear to be a leaf, and a leaf a stem; and a root may seem to be an organ of foliar (leafy) character, because it lives above the ground, is laminate and has a green colour. Examples are afforded by the 'leaves' of the prickly pear (a species of cactus), which are in reality flattened portions of stem of limited growth; and there are certain true leaves of quite a number of species of the genera *Lithops* and *Fenestraria* which are round or almost cylindrical in section. Or again, we could cite the epigeal (surface) roots of some orchids.

In all such cases, where there is any doubt as to the true nature of a particular organ, it is necessary to study its origins and in this way to discover by factual evidence whether we are dealing with a stem, a leaf or a root. Two organs of similar appearance, such as a potato and a turnip, are 'analogous' parts or organs, but these are of dissimilar nature because the potato originates from a thickened underground stem and is swollen with food reserves, whereas the turnip is a root although it also is heavy with copious food reserves. On the other hand, two organs of the same nature, such as the branch of a pear tree and the 'leaf' of a prickly pear, in spite of their obvious morphological differences, are 'homologous' because they are both stems. Ignoring the numerous homologues of minor importance, we shall here confine ourselves to the more common metamorphoses of stem, leaf and root.

The least drastic are those concerning dimensions and the consistency and manner of growth of stems. In dimensions we have stems which reach over a hundred yards in height, and others which are so short that they seem to be non-existent. Plants without apparent stems, such as the cowslip, daisy, primrose, or common plantain, are called 'acaulous'; those which have visible stems are called 'caulescent'. There are stems so feeble that they are unable to maintain themselves erect, and so they lie along the ground; these are 'decumbent' stems. Sometimes, these stems give off adventitious roots close to the nodes where these are in contact with damp ground, and in such cases we say they are 'runners' or root-forming stems. In this category are those which stretch some distance and bear few leaves, although they root easily, like the runners of strawberry plants, and they are called 'stolons'.

A similar type to this is the 'sarmentose stem' which throws out long, relatively thin branches, unable to support themselves; they need devices such as the 'sarmenta' (tendrils) of the grapevine or the thorns of the bramble to hold themselves up. See Fig. 30. Such plants generally give out many sarmenta, thanks to which, they climb up trees and using these as a support reach the top of the foliage in order to obtain maximum air and light; there are numerous species of these large creeping or climbing wild plants, especially in tropical forests. But there are climbing plants which avail themselves of other methods; that is, they climb by winding themselves around some conveniently sized trunk or stem; they are the 'twining' plants, the true

Fig. 30

Sarmentose stem of the bramble (*Rubus*) throwing out adventitious
roots from its end as this reaches the ground.

climbers. Many others have specialised organs for climbing, such as the familiar vine; its sarmenta do not simply
rest on a support, but grip it tightly by means of prehensile
tendrils.

At the other end of the scale we have stems which may
be enormously distended, replete with reserves of some
kind, such as water in cactus stems. In this way certain
Echinocactus come to have globular stems.

There are plants, such as broom (*Cytisus*) and dyer's
greenweed (*Genista*), with greatly reduced leaves, in which
foliar functions are carried out by the stems and the
branches. In *Genista*, the stems have a normal shape—
they are round and green, and consequently we cannot
talk of metamorphosis in this case. On the other hand,
there are stems performing similar functions which acquire
a flat form, as in the prickly pear and butcher's broom
(*Ruscus*). The stem of the prickly pear resembles a series
of large fleshy leaves, but they are really flattened stems
and are called 'cladodes'; those of certain species of *Ruscus*

Fig. 31

Kinds of stems. 1, Stem of a large climbing plant (*Ephedra altissima*)
supported by a savin (*Tetraclinis articulata*). 2, Laminar stem of another
climbing plant (*Bauhinia*), bearing knobby projections at intervals. In
Brazil this plant is known as 'the monkies' ladder' ('*escada dos macacos*').
3, Small branch of cedar with lateral branches of limited growth known
as 'brachyblasts'. 4, Twig with branches converted into spines (*Colletia
spinosa*). 5, Squat stem of *Euphorbia obesa*, partly buried. 6, Another
plant with branches converted into spines (*Centaurea spinosa*). Reduced.

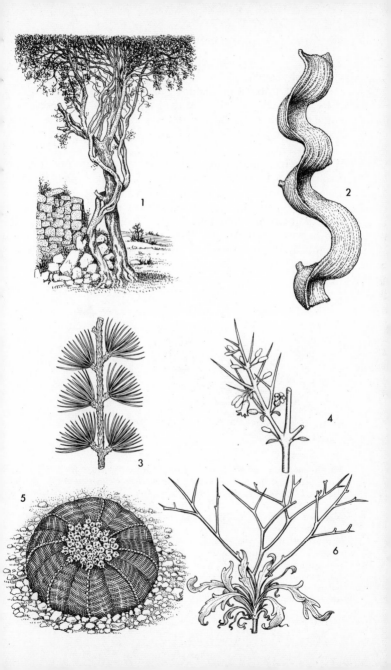

are more definitely shaped, smaller and thinner, and are called 'phylloclades'. Instead of fattening or broadening, stems and branches sometimes become pointed at their ends and form 'spines'. The true spines, such as those of furze and gorse are distinct from simple thorns, because the latter are just epidermal outgrowths, as on rose bushes. See Fig. 31.

Grapevine tendrils are also stem metamorphoses, and similar tendrils occur on many other plants which need them to clasp any support with which they may come into contact. The form of the tendrils varies, but they are always relatively thin and are endowed with an extraordinary sensitiveness, so that whenever they contact a likely support they twist themselves around it and grip it firmly. All such structures are included under the name of 'tendrils'.

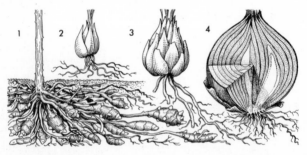

Fig. 32

Tubers and bulbs, some of which provide stores of reserve materials. 1, Subterranean stems of the Jerusalem artichoke (*Helianthus tuberosus*); the tips, in the form of stolons, swell and become tubers. 2, A very young bulb: in bulbs it is the leaves that swell. 3, A more developed bulb of the scaly type (white lily). 4, The tunicate bulb of the onion. Note the small, toughened, hemispherical base, corresponding with the stem, from which a bunch of equal roots springs; a variable number of thickened leaves (seven in the drawing) grow from its edges to form enclosing sheaths, which are the teguments of the onion. Two incipient shoots, one at each side, may also be seen; they stand out by their whiteness, the rest of the onion being very pale purple. The hemispherical stem at the base is also white. Reduced.

There are numerous plants which have subterranean stems and only their branches come above the surface of the ground; such stems are called 'rhizomes', and they grow horizontally. Examples are found among the grasses and reeds. That they are not roots is seen at once, because they have nodes and leaves—cataphylls which are not green and therefore unsuitable for photosynthesis purposes—and also buds which allow branching to take place. When they run horizontally and lengthen considerably, rhizomes are called 'stoloniferous'.

If a branch swells notably, and becomes full of food reserve materials, we have what is called a 'tuber'. Potatoes are underground tubers, although under certain circumstances they are produced and mature above ground. Tubers have a stem structure, and the so-called eyes of the potatoes are really buds from which new plants may be formed.

Both stem and leaves share in the production of 'bulbs'. Properly speaking, a bulb consists of a portion of a stem shaped like a plate or disc, sometimes flat and sometimes convex, from which spring roots, and of a group of thick, juicy leaves arranged circularly around it. In the bulb of the white lily, the numerous leaves composing it are loose and overlap each other, so we say that such a bulb is 'squamous' or 'scaly'. In the common onion, the outside leaves go completely around the stem disc and constitute the so-called skin of the onion; in this case we have a 'tunicate bulb', protected externally by those filmy red membranes which are the pellicles. See Figs. 32 and 33. Bulbs are formed under the ground, but similar organs exist which grow from the epigeal parts of the plant, for example, on leaves or in their axils, in certain inflorescences, etc. They are actually small buds, more or less thick and juicy, and these are also called bulbs.

Among the modified leaves we must take into account tendrils having foliar characteristics, such as those of peas and other leguminous plants, pumpkins, etc. These, instead of having a circular structure have a bilateral one similar to that of leaves. The same may be said about spines; there are spinous leaves with true spines, as in the leaves of the holly tree.

Rarely, leaves or parts of leaves are converted into receptacles of varying forms, most often resembling small leather wine bottles or pitchers; these are called 'ascidia'. The most notable ascidia are those of the carnivorous plants like certain species of the genus *Nepenthes*, which have a complex structure and secrete juices in which insects drown; and there is the tiny ascidium of the *Utricularias*, aquatic plants which trap and digest small organisms.

Finally, we come to root modifications, the most common of which is that affecting the shape, especially when the root acts as a storehouse of reserve food such as starch. They are called 'tuberous roots' and we see typical examples

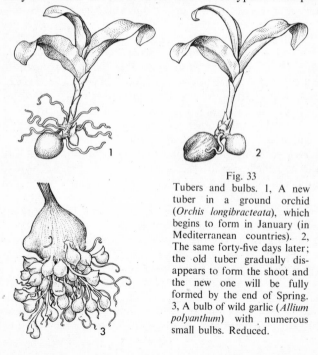

Fig. 33

Tubers and bulbs. 1, A new tuber in a ground orchid (*Orchis longibracteata*), which begins to form in January (in Mediterranean countries). 2, The same forty-five days later; the old tuber gradually disappears to form the shoot and the new one will be fully formed by the end of Spring. 3, A bulb of wild garlic (*Allium polyanthum*) with numerous small bulbs. Reduced.

in the turnip and parsnip. Tuberous roots may be distinguished from tubers by their structure and because they do not have either buds nor any sort of foliar appendage. (See Figs. 32 and 33). There are epigeal roots, which do not live under the ground but above it. We have already discussed adventitious roots, such as fulcral and columnar roots, which originate from the stem and branches and eventually find their way into the ground. But certain orchids have even more extraordinary roots, because not only are they epigeal, but they are green, and in cases where the plant has no leaves, these roots take over foliar functions.

In some of the flower-bearing, higher plants which thrive in more exotic climes than our own, there is such a profound degeneration of the plant body that we are unable to distinguish any kind of stem, leaves or roots. This is shown very clearly in the famous *Rafflesia arnoldii*, a plant found in the Malayan archipelago. The plant body, as such, has completely disappeared, and the growing apparatus, inserted into the body of another plant from which it sucks enough nourishment to sustain life, has become reduced to a few frayed threads which the observer would take to be fungal filaments were it not for the fact that, in due season, enormous flowers are produced. They are, indeed, the largest flowers known. On a smaller scale, the common dodder, which is parasitic on so many plants, has its plant body reduced to simple filamentous stems lacking chlorophyll, and it has neither leaves nor roots. But its place in the plant hierarchy is still quite recognisable by its flowers, the morphology of which entitles it to be ranked next to the Convolvulaceae.

6

Reproductive Organs

Being individuals, all living things, whether animal or vegetable, have a limited life. They are born and grow, only to fade away and die. Nevertheless, the tendency of all forms of life is to perpetuate themselves through their progeny, so that, though the individual may die the species lives on. The plant organs to which we have given our attention so far have been the vegetative organs—that is, those which enable the plant to grow and reach maturity. In the present chapter we shall consider the organs which enable the individual to ensure the perpetuation of its kind.

As a rule, the plant individual has a tendency to propagate its species by producing either direct successors, or the germs capable of becoming successors, in more than ample numbers. Frequently, among those plants which have an annual life-cycle, thousands upon thousands of germs are produced each year. However, not every plant yields such enormous quantities. Thus, among the simplest of vegetable organisms, such as the bacteria, each individual will give rise to only two new ones; from one cell come two cells. But the apparent paucity of this type of generation is amply compensated by the frequency with which it occurs, which may be every half-hour; another point is that the progenitor itself does not die but carries on its role of a germinative cell. In this and in all similar cases, a vegetable body—that is, the 'soma'—does not, strictly speaking, exist: all that exists is the 'germ'. Theoretically, vegetation consisting solely of germinal bodies never dies. If their existence is cut short it is by accident; under favourable conditions they neither grow old nor die.

MULTIPLICATION. The division of one unicellular organism into two individuals is the simplest form of multiplication among plants, and is most common among the lower members of the vegetable world; it is called 'fission' and is the simplest form of asexual reproduction.

In multicellular plants, and in colonies made up of autonomous cells, there is also 'fragmentation'. In this, there is no cellular division, but rather a separation of whole cells or groups of cells which may be called 'propagators'. This occurs, for example, in the Bryophyta. The propagators come in the same category as the 'cuttings' of the gardener, only here we have the intervention of man—who plants either pieces of the parent plant that show no signs of producing roots ('cuttings' proper), or pieces that have already sent out roots ('shoots', 'suckers').

But, in the majority of cases, the lower plants—algae, fungi, mosses—multiply by means of specialized germ cells, quite different from ordinary vegetative cells, and usually very small. They have been given the name of 'spores', and are produced in vast quantities inside closed receptacles called 'sporangia'; they are called 'conidiospores' when they originate from more or less complex supports called 'conidiophores'.

Spores and conidiospores, in spite of their small size, usually have the means of growing by themselves during the initial phases of their development. If the surrounding medium is sufficiently favourable, they will extract from it whatever is necessary to continue with this growth, but if it is not, then they die. More often than not, these germ cells are unable to withstand adverse circumstances, but some are covered with a strong impermeable membrane, inside which they may remain alive in spite of water losses which concentrate their substance, and they may also withstand very low temperatures and long periods of drought without any lessening of their vitality. These are called 'durable spores'. And because they are quite often not only resistant, but also require a period during which they must rest before recovering, they have also been called 'hypnospores' (from the Greek *hupnos*, sleep).

On the other hand, there are instances of germinal cells which not only do not sleep, but which, when viewed under the microscope, show such remarkable activity that they could be mistaken for animalcules. These germs are aquatic and only show this active movement when immersed. To effect movement they are equipped with long thread-like appendages called 'flagella', of which there is sometimes one but more commonly two. Occasionally they have a whole fringe of 'hairs' or 'vibratory cilia'. All these motile germinal bodies are grouped under the name of 'zoospores', and the sporangia from which they originate are called 'zoosporangia'.

Fission and the formation of all types of propagators, including the spores, conidiospores, zoospores, etc., constitute the various ways of multiplication.

REPRODUCTION. It happens quite frequently that germs are formed which, whether motile like the zoospores, or motionless, are unable to multiply. Even under the best possible conditions of temperature and available nourishment they just swim about in their medium or lie on the bottom without making the least effort to germinate. What is usually wrong in such cases is that something is missing and procreation cannot take place; they simply lack a mate to fulfil conjugal duties. In the simplest examples, the partners are alike; that is to say, we are unable to distinguish males from females, either by their shape, their dimensions or their behaviour. They meet, they couple or unite inextricably, and form one single organism containing the living substance of the original two—the 'zygote'. This manner of multiplying is called 'sexual multiplication', or more simply 'reproduction'. Let us say then that when there is no union of sexes plants 'multiply'; but if the germ requires the assistance of another, then they 'reproduce'.

ISOGAMY. The germ cells destined to come together with the object of increasing the numbers of the species—that is, the partners—are called 'gametes', and the receptacles in which they are formed are the 'gametangia'. When gametes are identical, we say that we have an instance of 'isogamy' or 'isogamous reproduction', which is the simplest sexual reproduction and is typical of the lower ranks of the Vegetable Kingdom.

HETEROGAMY. In all other cases—that is, when the conjugal pair are more or less different—we have the phenomenon of 'heterogamy' or 'heterogamous reproduction'. Heterogamy becomes manifest when, although both gametes may be morphologically equal, there is a difference in behaviour or in size, or in both. The first manifestations of femaleness become apparent in a certain increase in size of the female gamete, and when it moves, in a certain sluggishness in its movements. The female gamete travels either with reluctance or not at all, while the male moves with obvious agility.

Masculine initiative begins then, on the first fringes of heterogamy, and as we ascend the scale of increasingly complex morphological differentiation, we find the female becoming increasingly more passive until she is absolutely static, even to the point of having lost all her locomotory organs, while the male gamete, preserving these intact, behaves like some kind of water-sprite and maintains full activity. The passive female gamete, thus differentiated, has been given the name of 'ovule'—the 'ovum' of the animal kingdom; and her consort, motile and agile, is the 'spermatozoid'—the 'spermatozoon' of animals, including man.

Organs and organic apparatuses dedicated to multiplication and to reproduction vary considerably from one group to another within the vegetable hierarchy. We shall only be able to treat them with brevity in a book of this scope, but may point out here that though the production of spermatozoons has persisted to the highest ranks in the animal kingdom, the plants have pursued other lines of development, and the spermatozoids, which necessarily demand a fluid medium for their activities, have lost their

faculty of movement in the higher plants, and are conducted to the ovule along the so-called pollen-tube.

THE FLOWER. In the higher plants, the mating of the two
germ cells is prepared for in advance by certain organs,
whose propagative functions give the 'flower' the sole
reason for its existence.

A flower, or rather the simplest form of the flower, consists of one or several stamens, and one or several pistils,
situated at the end of a short branch. The 'stamens' consist
of an 'anther' and (usually) a supporting 'filament'. The
anther contains four receptacles or 'microsporangia', also
called 'pollen sacs'. Inside the pollen sacs spores are produced, often in great profusion. These are the 'microspores'
or pollen grains, to give them their more familiar name.
The pollen grains are destined to engender the male gametes, without cilia or flagella; for this reason, flowers with
stamens are called 'male flowers'.

The 'pistils' vary in form from one species to another.
Normally, they consist of an elongated column of tissue
the upper part of which is called the 'style'. This expands
at its tip to form the globular or segmented 'stigma'. The
basal part of the pistil, the 'ovary', is where the rudimentary seeds are formed, at this stage called 'ovules'. For this
reason, flowers bearing pistils are called 'female flowers'.

In the simpler flowering plants, those belonging to the
Gymnosperms, the flowers are either male or female, and
are therefore called 'unisexual flowers'. Some of the families
of Angiosperms also fall into this category, but they occupy
inferior positions in the hierarchy.

There are species of plants which have male and female
flowers distributed on the same individual, which enables
it to reproduce fairly easily because both sexes are close
at hand, so to speak. In other species, however, this is not
so; the individual plant is either male or female, some
plants will producing only staminate flowers and others
only pistillate flowers. The plant which has flowers of
both sexes is called 'monoecious'; that which produces

either male or female flowers, 'dioecious'. Any individual of a monoecious type of plant is self-sufficient as far as the reproduction of the species is concerned, but this is not so with a dioecious plant, which requires the co-operation of an individual of the opposite sex.

In the great majority of the higher plants, flowers are produced which bear stamens and pistils together on the same stalk. This is very convenient when the time comes to engender new individuals, because the stamens and pistils are right next to each other on the same support. Such are called 'hermaphrodite' or 'perfect' flowers. As proof of the success achieved in the plant world by utilising this juxtaposition of components, one need only think of the innumerable species with hermaphrodite flowers now in existence. The number of species which have but one sex to an individual are in a relatively small minority.

However the success of the combination of the sexes in a single flower was not quite all that might be desired. When we have in our garden a single individual of a certain species and wait patiently for it to bear fruit, so that with a large quantity of seeds we may have many more plants of the same species in the following year, we may be disappointed to see the immature fruits fall to the ground one by one. This is not always the fault of the environment, nor may it be due to poor acclimatization of a species brought from distant lands—nor, even, that it is planted in soil not to its liking. It will be none of these things, because we have only to introduce another individual of the same species into the same flower bed to see our failure turn into success as if by magic.

So we can see that the success achieved by the hermaphroditic flowers was not as perfect as it might have been, because, very often the presence of other individuals is necessary. It is by the exchange of the pollens that the fertility of the plant is ensured or greatly increased. Sometimes this rule is broken and it happens that the pistil of a hermaphroditic flower is quite fertile with pollen from another flower on the same plant. This has been abundantly proved by 'artificial pollination'. Pollination is the transfer of pollen from the anther to the stigma. To do this artificially all that is needed is a very fine camel-hair brush with which to lift the pollen from the anthers, already mature and open, and deposit it very gently on to the sticky surface of the stigma.

THE PERIANTH. Long before man appeared on the earth, other pollinators were in action. They were extraordinarily efficient, and to them the Plant Kingdom is indebted for much of its present-day finery. This success was due, on the part of the plants, to two developments. First came the production of nectar, and then the perianth.

Nectar is a sweet, sugary, aromatic fluid, greatly to the liking of some insects, and of man himself who takes it after it has been imbibed and converted into honey by the insect. These sugary nectars accumulate in the vicinity of the flower, and are of considerable importance for its development. The insect which settles on a nectar-bearing flower and drinks the nectar, then visits another flower of the same species. It becomes an involuntary pollinator because with this constant coming and going it cannot help but come into intimate contact with anthers and stigmas. As a pollinator, the insect is efficient enough to counteract the first signs of slackening vigour in the hermaphrodite flower.

But the insect, in spite of its acute sense of smell, is unable to see from a distance anything that could serve it as a guide to help it towards the desired goal. At close quarters it can appreciate colour, tone and shade, but shape is less useful to it. At this juncture we may ask our-ourselves how plants that have nectar to offer can provide useful signs for the guidance of the insect pollinators. A group of leaves made more conspicuous by means of colour—say one or more hypsophylls next to the flower— would mean that the nectar would be much more easily found, and some plants therefore provide such leaves. The insect's visits are thus multiplied and are of mutual benefit to it and to the plant, the insect being able to regale itself with the nectar, and the plant gaining from the encounter an increased fertility. Also, being fertilised in this way the plant is ensured of a considerable increase in its progeny, and those whose flowers visually advertise the presence of nectar are, in fact, gradually superseding those

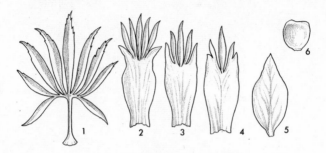

Fig. 34

Leaf metamorphosis. 1, A normal leaf, or normophyll, of hellebore (*Helleborus foetidus*). 2 to 5, Bracteal leaves, or hypsophylls, of the same plant, those on the left being farthest from the flower. 6, Floral leaf of the perianth. Reduced.

that rely instead on the distribution of their pollen by the wind. These last produce enormous quantities of pollen, which is scattered wastefully in all directions on the chance that a few grains may happen to fall on the right stigma. So, first there was nectar, and afterwards came those brightly coloured hypsophylls, which, because they are found in a circle around the base of the flower, have been given the name of 'perianth' (from the Greek *peri* around, *anthos* flower). See Figs. 34 and 35.

There exist numerous plants, such as all kinds of pines and spruce, whose flowers lack a perianth, and others, such as the black poplar and the willow, in which the flowers are quite rudimentary. These flowers are said to be 'naked'. Among the rest, the perianth may appear in many variations, and with these we shall now concern ourselves.

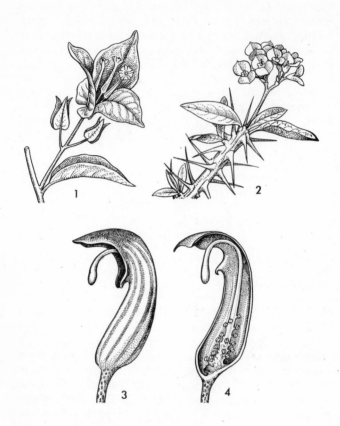

Fig. 35

'Flowers' which are not flowers. 1, Three small true flowers of *Bougainvillea* surrounded by three large violet bracts, which appear to be the real flower. 2, Group of inconspicuous flowers of *Euphorbia splendens*, each enclosed by two opposing scarlet bracts. 3, Inflorescence of *Arisarum vulgare*, with one large, enveloping, closed bract called a 'spathe'. 4, The same sectioned longitudinally to show the axis of the inflorescence, the 'spadix', at the base of which the true flowers, which are very small and unisexual, are visible. Slightly reduced.

The simplest perianth consists of several parts arranged around the plant's sex organs and forming a single verticil. Sometimes such flowers, called 'monochlamydeous' (that is to say, having a single covering), are inconspicuous both in respect of the small size of the parts of the perianth and their rather dull colours, which may be green or greyish. They generally send their pollen into the air because they have nothing attractive to lure insects. When the perianth is composed of two verticils, we say that the flower is 'dichlamydeous', and it may be that the inner and outer verticils have the same or nearly the same shape, colour and texture, in which case they are said to be 'homocheamydeous'. Again, both verticils may be totally different in form and colour, and these are called 'heterochlamydeous' flowers.

When a flower has a simple perianth, or if, though double, it is homochlamydeous, we say it has a 'perigynium'. The dicotyledonous angiosperms lower down in the scale, such as all types of oak and holm-oak, the chestnut, nettles, etc., are monochlamydeous, and all these have very inconspicuous perigynia. Lilies of all classes, and tulips, etc., are also monochlamydeous plants, but they have large and ostentatious perigynia. In every case, the leaves of the perigynium are called 'tepals'.

CALYX AND COROLLA. In those plants which possess dichlamydeous flowers, the perianth is in the majority of cases heterochlamydeous, with the outer verticil quite distinct from the inner one. The external verticil is practically always composed of floral leaves, or green antophylls, the foliar origin of which is immediately obvious not only from its colour but also from its structure: it is called the 'calyx', and its components are the 'sepals'.

The second floral verticil, the inner one, is the 'corolla', and it may usually be distinguished by the splendour of its colouring, which is very rarely green, and by the large size of its units, the 'petals'.

The calyx is a perianthic verticil whose principal func-

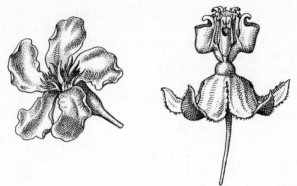

Fig. 36

Left: Flower of rosebay, with the corolla symmetrical around the floral axis but with no plane of symmetry, and having appendages called 'ligulas' round the 'throat'. *Right*: Flower of *Asclepias*, gamopetalous, actinomorphic, and with an extra circle of parts—the 'corona'—of staminal origin. Rosebay natural size; *Asclepias* enlarged.

tion is to protect the delicate flower from inclement weather. On the other hand, the corolla is a spectacular verticil which is always present in nectarferous flowers; its function consists principally in signalling to insect pollinators the presence of flowers and nectar.

The perigynium—and, when the perianth is dichlamydeous, the calyx and the corolla—may be perfectly regular; that is to say, it is either 'actinomorphic', having all the

Fig. 37

Kinds of flowers. 1, Cactus flower (*Trichocereus spachianus*) with an elaborate perianth containing numerous stamens and a pistil with fifteen stigmas (corresponding to as many carpels). 2, Ordinary (actinomorphic) flower of *Fuchsia*, with the receptacle mainly tubular and the calyx and corolla of four parts each, the latter having free petals. There are eight stamens and a pistil with four carpels. 3, Actinomorphic flowers, largely tubular (gamopetalous), of *Plumbago capensis*. 4, Gamopetalous, zygomorphic flower of *Linaria*, showing the long spur. 5, Dialypetalous, zygomorphic flower (Caesalpiniaceae) of carinate prefloration. 6, Gamopetalous, actinomorphic, funnel-shaped flower of *Pharbitis*. 7, Gamopetalous, zygomorphic flower of *Celsia sinuata*, with a very short tube.

units equal and evenly arranged around the axis, or 'zygomorphic', having its parts arranged asymmetrically so that the flower can be divided into equal halves in only one plane. In many cases the perigynium is completely asymmetrical, without any plane of symmetry at all, as, for instance, in the so-called Indian Shot of the genus *Canna*. The perianths of the lilies, carnation, wild rose, strawberry, cabbage, etc., are actinomorphous; those of orchids, sage, rosemary, honeysuckle, foxglove, etc., are zygomorphis. For other examples see Fig. 36.

There are also perigynia, calyces and corollas with the tepals, sepals and petals free from each other, without any kind of join; then we say that they are 'dialyphylls', or more particularly, 'dialytepals', 'dialysepals' and 'dialypetals', respectively. In other perianths, the parts of each of the verticils may be joined together to form greater or smaller parts, producing single perigynia, calyces and corollas, which are given the names of 'gamotepals', 'gamosepals' and 'gamopetals', respectively; variants of these names are 'syntepals', 'synsepals' and 'sympetals'. When dealing with dicotyledonous plants it is usual to classify them as dialypetals and synpetals, because in general all the plants in a family agree as to one characteristic—that is, in the independence or harmony of the parts of its flowers. In contrast, in the *Liliaceae* we see two types of perianth: dialytepalous in the white lily and syntepalous in the hyacinth. Some typical flower forms are illustrated in Fig. 37.

PREFLORATION. In a flower bud, the name 'prefloration' is applied to the relative positioning of the sepals or the petals of each floral verticil. We say in the bud, because in the completely opened flower the sepals and the petals have often separated so far from each other that it is difficult to determine the prefloration. See Fig. 38.

There are six main kinds of prefloration: valvate, contorted, quincuncial, imbricate, vexillate, and carinate. In 'valvate' prefloration, the parts of the flower may touch at

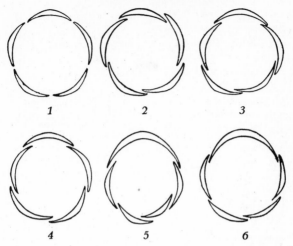

Fig. 38

Types of prefloration. 1, Valval, in which the antophylls touch at the edges. 2, Contorted, where the parts are covered on one edge but exposed on the other. 3, Quincuncial, with two external parts, two internal, and the other half internal and half external. 4, Imbricate, with one part external, one internal, and the other three half internal and half external. 5, Vexillate, typical of Papilionaceous plants with a superior external petal, the 'vexil', two laterals called 'wings', and two inferior ones which are internal and constitute the 'carina'. 6, Carinate, with the carina of the previous inflorescence external and the vexil inside. (See Fig. 37–5).

the edges, but none of them overlaps a neighbouring part. In the 'contorted' each part lies above that which follows and below that which precedes it, as if they had all been twisted. In the 'quincuncial', two parts are completely external, two internal, and the fifth part internal on one edge and external on the other. In the 'imbricate', there is one part external on both edges, another next to this completely internal, and the three remaining are external on one side and internal on the other. The 'vexillate' prefloration differs from the imbricate in that the part which is completely internal does not lie next to the external one, but right on top. Finally, in the 'carinate' prefloration the external part of the vexillate prefloration is now internal, and one of the lower parts now passes to the exterior. Prefloration is important because very often it is used to classify plants; thus, the *Malvaceae* are valvate, the *Gentianaceae* are contorted, and the *Leguminosae* may have either vexillate or carinate preflorations.

THE ANDROECIUM. Taking the verticils from the outside towards the inside of the flower, after the calyx and the corolla we come to the 'androecium'. The androecium is composed of véry much changed leaves called 'stamens', bearing pollen, as we have already mentioned. Mostly, they do not have a laminar form like the sepals and the petals but are composed of filaments (which may be quite short or even absent) and 'anthers', situated at the tip. The anther is the most important part of the stamen, since it is here that the pollen is formed. See Fig. 39.

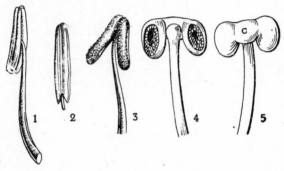

Fig. 39

Kinds of stamens. 1, *Colchicum*, with its long filament joined to the back of the anther. 2, Saffron, with the filament joined to the base of the anther. 3, *Tecoma*, with diverging thecas in the anther. 4 and 5, Marjoram, seen from in front and behind, with the thecas separated by the connective, *c*, here well developed. Magnified.

Comparing the phanerogams, or flower-bearing plants, with the ferns, which produce two kinds of spores, 'microspores' and 'macrospores', the stamens are classed as 'microsporophylls'—that is, leaves which produce microspores. The four cavities forming the anther, which we have called 'pollen sacs', are really 'microsporangia', and the pollen grains are microspores.

Perianthic verticils have a number of parts which vary from one family to another; usually they have four or five. In the androecium we find from one to any number of stamens, the number being called 'indefinite' if it exceeds twenty.

In exactly the same way as in the floral verticils, the androecium may be actinomorphic or zygomorphic; it may have free or joined stamens, and in the latter case the stamens may be united by the filaments or by the anthers, or even by both. The androecium is said to be 'monadelphous' when all the filaments of the stamens are connected in one piece or bundle, 'diadelphous' if they form two bundles, and 'polyadelphous' if they constitute several bundles. Lastly, the stamens of the androecium may all be of the same length, or some may be longer than others. This inequality in length gives rise to three designations: when there are several stamens and one is markedly longer than the rest, the androecium is called 'monodynamic'; when, there being four stamens altogether, two are longer than the rest it is called 'didynamic'; when the androecium is composed of six stamens, four long and two short, it is called 'tetradynamic'.

In the anther, besides the pollen sacs, there is a portion of sterile tissue called the 'connective', which joins the two halves or 'thecae'. In nearly every case, each theca is composed of two pollen sacs, which, as they ripen, form a single cavity filled with pollen. When the time comes, both thecae open by the formation of various longitudinal slits—or, less frequently, by means of valves or pores—as in the laurels and heathers, respectively. These openings are normally made facing the centre of the flower, and the anthers are 'introrse'; more rarely they open towards the outside, and these are called 'extrorse'.

Generally speaking, if the corolla is sympetalous, attention must be paid to the length of the stamens in relation to it. The stamens may rise above it and become visible from outside, so we say they are 'exserted'. If they remain hidden within the corolla and invisible to our gaze, they are 'enclosed'. There is also a relation between the number of stamens and the corolla. A flower which has the same number of stamens as petals is 'isostamineous'; sometimes, however, there are twice as many stamens, and we say it is 'diplostamineous', or there may even be several times as many and the flower is 'polystamineous'. The Ranuncul-aceae, with five petals and an indefinite number of stamens, have polystamineous flowers; the Papilionaceae, with five petals and ten stamens, are diplostamineous; the Violaceae, also having five petals but with only five stamens, are isostamineous. In diplostamineous flowers, the stamens generally occupy two verticils: an external verticil with the stamens placed between the petals, and an internal verticil which have the stamens situated in front of the petals. Among the phanerogams, we regard the 'perfect' flower as having two perianthic verticils, the calyx and the corolla; two verticils of stamens; and a fifth and innermost verticil comprising the gynaeceum.

POLLEN. The microspores or pollen grains of the phane-rogams are unicellular at the time they are formed. Their dimensions, shape and surface-markings vary considerably from one genus to another, and even more so from one family to another. There are pollen grains so small that they measure only two thousandths of a millimetre across; others are relatively big, about a quarter of a millimetre and quite visible to the naked eye. Frequently, the pollen of certain plants is typical of its family and it bears definite characteristics which are of great importance in plant classification. In the Acanthaceae, for example, the pollen varies a good deal, but, on the other hand, in the Grami-neae there is very little variation.

A pollen grain is normally rounded or oblong in shape, but its tough outer coat, called the 'exine', is covered with characteristic engravings and reliefs—such as wrinkles,

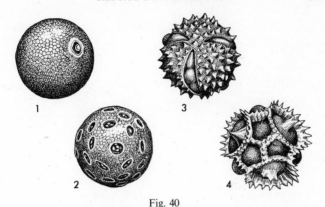

Fig. 40

Pollen grains. 1, *Phleum pratense*. 2, *Salsola pestifer*. 3, *Haplopappus acaulis*. 4, *Scolymus hispanicus*. Highly magnified; sizes not proportionate. (*After* Wodehouse).

pores, prongs, warts, etc. See Fig. 40. The exine is formed from a material known as 'sporopollinine' consisting largely of cutin, which is non-rotting and capable of remaining intact for thousands of years. Pollen discovered in peat bogs has been found quite unchanged in spite of its enormous age. The annual growth of a peat bog can be determined very precisely, and experts who have made a study of the subject are able to ascertain not only the changes in the vegetation during the accumulation of the peat, but also its age at any stage. Further, because practically all the species identified in peat are still living and we know the type of climate they prefer, it is possible to state how the climate must have changed since the peat first began to form.

Underneath the exine, the pollen grain is protected by yet another membrane, but this time a thinner and much less resistant one, called the 'intine'; this is composed of pectin.

Looking at the grains of pollen through a microscope, we can make out with relative ease certain 'areolae' or depressions of a lighter colour, like pale crescents. At these points, called 'germinal pores', the exine is thin, which means that they are areas of less resistance and can allow easier egress for the 'pollen tube', which, when conditions are favourable, will emerge from the grain as it germinates.

THE GYNAECEUM. Just as the androecium consists of pollinate leaves or stamens, so the gynaeceum is composed of 'carpellary' leaves, or 'carpels'. Often, the metamorphosis which gave rise to the transformation from ordinary leaves into carpellary leaves has not been quite so drastic as that which led to the formation of the stamens; taking a peep into our own domestic kitchen, we can get a good idea of this by examination of the carpellary leaves of some of our leguminous vegetables—the beans and peas. The pod of these vegetables consists of a single carpellary leaf with all the characteristics of a leaf. In this leaf we can easily recognise the mid-rib which runs the whole length of the pod on the side without seeds. Two marginal veins or a duplicated mid-rib runs along the opposite side, and it is here that the seeds are produced. When the pod is quite mature, we may also see in it the lateral veins which spring from the mid-rib and run across to the margins.

The carpellary leaf is joined at the edges to form a closed cavity called the 'ovary'. Usually it ends in a sort of slender column called the 'style' which is expanded at its tip to form a rounded head known as the 'stigma'. This is the case when the gynaeceum has only one carpel, as in the Leguminosae, but in the majority of cases there are several carpels. In the hellebores and the peonies, two or more may be formed; in the anemones and the buttercups there are several. In all these examples, the carpellary leaves remain quite free.

When the gynaeceum is composed of several carpels, the elements may join together to form a single ovary. The fusion can extend to the style and to the stigma as well as the region of the ovary; there are, of course, ovaries with several styles and several stigmas—one for each carpel—and again, ovaries with a single style and a single stigma. Sometimes, the style is missing and the stigma is located directly on top of the ovary.

The 'pistil', so called because of its resemblance to a pestle, may be said to be a monocarpellate gynaeceum, or a polycarpellate gynaeceum when the carpels are joined together in one piece. When the carpels remain independent, there are as many pistils as carpels. However, frequently the terms pistil and gynaeceum are synonymous.

The concrescent carpels may coalesce in two ways: by their borders to form a single cavity, or by their sides, where each carpel has already closed, thereby constituting an ovary with several cavities. In this case, it is said that the ovary has 'closed carpels'; if they remain open, then the ovary has 'open carpels'.

The marginal veins, more or less turgid and swollen, where the rudimentary seeds are formed, are called 'placentae', and the thread or stalk by which the seeds or ovules are attached to the placenta has been given the name of 'funiculus' or 'umbilical cord'—names which have endured since the eighteenth century, when efforts were made to correlate vegetable reproductive organs with the supposedly corresponding organs in animals. The location or disposition of the placentae in the ovary varies from one genus to another and from one family to another, and is called 'placentation'. In ovaries having open carpels, the placentation is called 'parietal', because the rudimentary seeds spring from the walls of the ovary, as they do, for example in the violets and the pansy. In those with closed carpels, having the placentae on the edges of the carpels, they seem to arise from the ovarian axis, and for this reason the placentation is said to be 'axile'. When the ovary is unilocular (i.e., having one cavity) and the rudimentary seeds spring from the centre, it is 'central'.

RUDIMENTARY SEEDS. These are the incipient seeds, which in the angiosperms are found within the ovary; in the gymnosperms they are left exposed because these plants do not have ovarian cavities. We have already pointed out that, in the normal way, each rudimentary seed is joined to the placenta by a small thread called the funiculus, which is well supplied with conducting elements.

The most important component of the rudimentary seed is the 'nucellus', which is composed of a great number of small cells and one cell conspicuously larger than the rest, called the 'embryo sac mother-cell'. If the pollen grain can be compared with a microspore of the heterosporous ferns, then the embryo sac mother-cell may be said to be homologous with a macrospore. In the embryo sac, a special cell is differentiated and comes to lie at the extreme end; this is the 'egg cell', and it is generally situated between two other cells called 'synergids' or 'synergid cells'. At the other end of the sac three more cells are formed—the 'antipodal cells'. Towards the centre of the embryo sac is the so-called 'secondary nucleus', because each sac, at the commencement of its development, has a 'primary nucleus', which, after three consecutive divisions, produces eight nuclei. Three or these constitute the egg cell and the two synergids, three the antipodal cells, and the two remaining fuse together and form the secondary nucleus of the embryo sac.

The nucellus is protected by one or two coverings, called the 'integuments', which surround it completely except for a point situated at the opposite end to that attached to the funiculus. At this point a narrow canal called the 'micropyle', which reaches as far as the nucellus, is formed.

The nucellus, surrounded by its one or both integuments, is joined to these at its base; the conducting elements which reach the rudimentary seed come from the placenta, and following the funiculus they disperse throughout the integuments from a point at the base of the nucellus called the 'chalaza', but without penetrating the nucellus itself. See Fig. 41.

There are three kinds of rudimentary seeds. Those which, being quite straight, have the micropyle exactly opposite the base or the point of junction of the nucellus

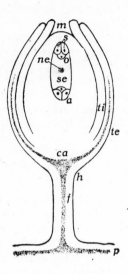

Fig. 41

Section of a rudimentary seed. At the foot is the placenta, *p*, from which arises the funiculus, *f*, supporting the rudimentary seed. The point where the funiculus joins the rudimentary seed is called the 'hilum', *h*. The chalaza, *ca*, lies below the nucellus, which is protected by two integuments, the internal, *ti*, and the external, *te*, which terminate at the tip of the micropyle, *m*. Inside the nucellus is seen the embryonic sac, *se*, and in this lies the secondary nucleus, *ne*, the ovule, *o*, and the two synergids, *s*. At the other end of the embryonic sac are the three antipodal cells, *a*.

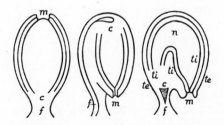

Fig. 42

Rudimentary seeds. 1, Orthotropic. 2, Anatropic. 3, Campylotropic.

with the funiculus, are called 'orthotropic'. When the nucellus has made a half turn so that the micropyle is touching the point of insertion of the funiculous, we say that it is 'anatropic'. In cases where the micropyle and point of junction of the funiculus are also very close, but owing to a curvature of the rudimentary seed the nucellus is not quite as straight as in the two previous cases, it is 'campylotropic'. Fig. 42.

Each carpel may form one or several rudimentary seeds; in other words, the carpels may be 'uniovulate', 'biovulate', etc., or, in the case of a great number of seeds, 'pluri- ovulate' or 'multiovulate'.

THE RECEPTACLE. The enlarged end of the pedicel or peduncle, to which the flower parts such as the androecium and the gynaeceum are attached, is called the 'receptacle', and it may be considered as a sort of marriage bed, in which the nuptials are consummated. In the unisexual flowers, which are in the minority, there is a receptacle for each of the sexes; in the hermaphrodite flowers the recep- tacle forms a common base for both sexes. But the shape or form of the receptacle really does not depend on what is going to occupy it, and further, it varies in an enormous number of ways from one plant to another.

There are flat or slightly convex receptacles, in which the perianth arises around them, a little below the androecium and the gynaeceum, and in such cases we say the flower is 'hypogynous'. Other receptacles may be more or less con- cave, so that the gynaeceum is in the deepest part of it with the perianth growing around the edges and around the pistil or pistils; this type of flower is said to be 'perigynous'. When the receptacle is very deep and becomes fused with the pistil, both the androecium and the perianth seem to rise from the top of the gynaeceum and the flower is called 'epigynous'. Epigynous flowers have an 'inferior' ovary, because it is situated below the level of insertion of the perianth and the stamens; and in other cases, no matter how deep the gynaeceum may be, because there is no fusion

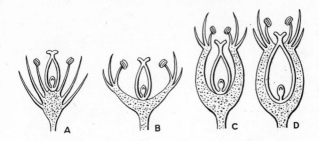

Fig. 43

The position of the ovary with respect to the receptacle, which is shown stippled. If the receptacle is convex, as at *A*, the flower (sepals, petals and stamens) is called 'hypogynous'. If it is concave (*B, C* and *D*), the ovary is free in 'perigynous' flowers (*B* and *C*) or fused with the receptacle in 'epigynous' flowers, in which the ovaries are inferior (*D*).

with the receptacle the ovary is called 'superior'. See Fig. 43.

In some plants, for example the caper, the receptacle elongates disproportionately and raises the ovary high in the air; in this and in similar cases it is given the name of 'gynophore' when the plant is in flower, and 'carpophore' if it is bearing fruit. In a few species, the stamens are also inserted into this elongated receptacle, which means that it bears both the androecium and the gynaeceum, and for this reason it is called an 'androgynophore'.

In contrast, the receptacle in some families becomes dilated into a flat plate and constitutes a 'hypogynous disc', or, because it may be where the sugary fluid, the nectar, is concentrated, the 'nectariferous disc'. In the umbelliferous plants, the disc is 'epigynous', because the ovary is inferior in this family. Nectaries are not always disc-shaped, however. Sometimes they have other forms; for example, they are like horns in the hellebores and are found in the petals in many buttercups, where they can be seen at the bases of the petals like small sacs. There are also 'extrafloral nectaries', which are quite separated from the flower. See Fig. 44.

Fig. 44

Flowers of black hellebore (*Helleborus niger*), composed of a perianth of five sepals and numerous stamens (seen in the flower on the left). The several carpels can be seen in the flower on the right, in which the stamens have been shed. In these flowers the petals are reduced to nectaries in the shape of small horns, of which one is shown between the two flowers.

ALTERNATION OF FLORAL COMPONENTS. When we were discussing the position of the stamens, we mentioned that it was usual for the first verticil (if the flower has two) to alternate with the petals in such a way that between every two petals there appeared a stamen; and between each two stamens of the first verticil, there arose one of the second verticil. If the flower is 'homomerous'—that is, if all its verticils are composed of the same number of components—this alternation is normal.

FLORAL DIAGRAMS. Schematic representation of foliar sections by means of orthogonal projection on a plane, which we have referred to in connection with phyllotaxis, may also be applied to the study of the flower, since this is a kind of short branch, with the phyllomes represented by antophylls or floral leaves. In floral diagrams, the sections corresponding to sepals are conveniently represented by white crescents; petals by black crescents; the anthers of the stamens by white sections; and the gynaeceum is

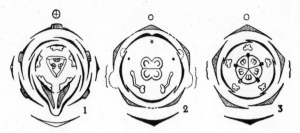

Fig. 45

Floral diagrams. 1, Violet, a zygomorphic flower with the lower petal spur-shaped, the nectaries being directed from the two front stamens into the spur; the ovary is tricarpellate and unilocular. 2, Zygomorphic flower of a labiate (*Salvia*), with two fertile stamens in front; two others, present in other labiates, are represented by points, and a fifth (shown by an asterisk) is abortive. 3, Flower of Canadian elder tree, actinomorphic and pentamerous in all its verticils. (*After* Eichler).

shown in the centre of the diagram by a section of the ovary. See Fig. 45.

From a study of a diagram a very good idea can be obtained of the structure of a flower. From it one can deduce its symmetry, the number of components in each verticil, its prefloration, its fusion or otherwise; the position of the stamens relative to the perianth, their concrescence or separation, their joining with the corolla or their independence, whether the anthers are introrse or extrorse, the number of pollen sacs or of thecas in each anther, etc., the number of carpels and cavities in the ovary, if it is apocarpous (that is, with free carpels) or syncarpous (with united carpels), the placentation and so on.

FLORAL FORMULAE. Although not quite so expressive as the diagrams, the 'floral formulae' enable one to identify a floral structure by means of abbreviations and numbers. As a general rule, the calyx is represented by the letter K, the corolla by C, the perigynium by P, the androecium by A, and the gynaeceum by G. Thus, the flower of the poppy, which has two sepals, four petals in two verticils, an

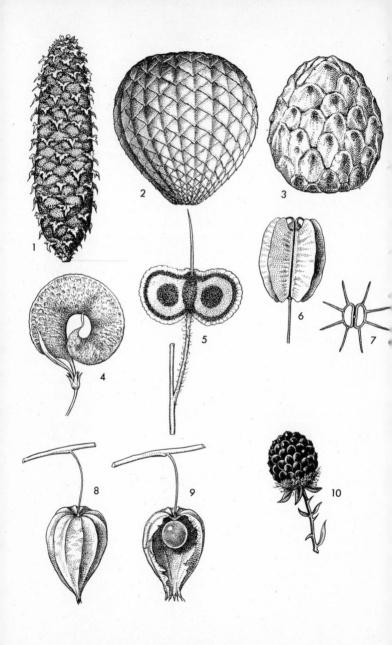

indefinite number of stamens, and from five to eighteen carpels, has the following floral formula: $K_2 C_{2+2} A \infty G (5-18)$. The brackets which enclose the number of carpels indicate that these have been combined into a single ovary, and the horizontal line underneath shows that the ovary is superior.

CARPOLOGY. When the ovule of the rudimentary seed has been fertilised, it develops until it has become a seed proper, and at the same time the ovary undergoes a series of metamorphoses and changes into a fruit. We will therefore define a 'fruit' as an ovary with the ovules fertilised and the rudimentary seeds converted into seeds. 'Carpology' concerns itself with the study of the various kinds of fruit.

A fruit is composed of two essential parts: the 'pericarp', constituted by the walls of the ovary more or less expanded and developed, and the seed or seeds which are enclosed within it. Some typical fruits are illustrated in Fig. 46.

In those fruits which have a very well developed pericarp, such as the peach, one can distinguish three parts: the skin, which is peeled off and thrown away, called the 'epicarp'; the pulp of the fruit—in the peach, the flesh, which is the edible portion—called the 'mesocarp'; and the 'stone', which is the innermost part of the fruit, or the 'endocarp'. Inside the endocarp is the seed.

The peach is a fleshy or 'indehiscent' fruit; that is to say, it does not split open when ripe. Other fruits are dry, dehiscent or have other characteristics. The way in which fruits split open is important in their classification. Some

Fig. 46

Kinds of fruits. 1, Cone of the common spruce (*Abies alba*), a false fruit because it is not formed by carpels. 2, Fruit of a palm (*Coelococcus*) with a hard shell. 3, Soft fruit of the cherimoya or custard-apple (*Anona cherimolia*). 4, Falciform legume (*Medicago arborea*). 5, Silicle (*Biscutella auriculata*). 6, Diachene winged fruit of an umbellifer (*Laserpitium*). 7, A transverse section of the same. 8 and 9, Berry enclosed in an acrescent calyx (*Physalis alkekengi*). 10, Multidrupe of bramble.

of them do so by making one or more longitudinal fissures; others by means of transverse fissures. Again, there are those which form pores or small openings at some part of the pericarp. Thus, we say that the dehiscence is 'longitudinal', 'transversal' or 'foraminal', respectively.

When classifying fruits, one has to take into account the number of carpels in the ovary, the dehiscence in relation to the placing of the fissures in relation to the carpels, etc. In dry fruits and those having longitudinal dehiscence, for example, it is of great importance to know whether the fissure is formed on the back of the carpel or at its edges, and finally if the thin walls of the carpels have been split along planes parallel to the axis of the fruit.

Among the dry and dehiscent fruits, the simplest of all is the 'follicle'; it is formed from a single carpel, which, folding over and joining along its edges, forms a single cavity. On ripening, the fused edges come away again and the fruit opens. The placentae and the seeds are located along the same edges. There are some species of larkspur (*Delphinium*) which have follicles for fruit. In other species

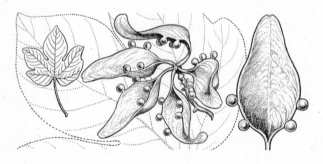

Fig. 47

Fruit of *Sterculia acerifolia*, composed of five follicles which have opened on reaching maturity. On the right, the foliar morphology of the carpel can be clearly seen, with rudimentary seeds at its edges already changed into seeds. The shapes of the normophylls or ordinary leaves are very different from those of the carpellary leaves and can be easily distinguished.

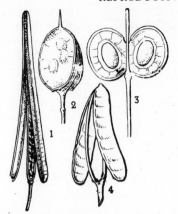

Fig. 48
Dry fruits. 1, Silique (*Arabis perfoliata*). 2, Silicle (*Lunaria biennis*). 3, Didymous silicle (*Biscutella*). 4, Silique of celidonia (*Chelidonium*), without the partition found in the Cruciferae.

of the same genus, in the peonies and the hellebores, in fact in all genera of the Ranunculaceae, the fruits are 'plurifollicular', because instead of one, several follicles are formed in each flower. See also Fig. 47. The Leguminosae are no more complicated, because they too only have a single carpel, but on ripening they open in two places; that is to say, they split along the suture formed by the carpellary edges and along the mid-rib running down its length. The legume or true pod is typical of the Leguminosae. In a fully developed pod, the marginal veins are always distinct from the mid-rib, for once the pod has been opened and split in two, it is seen that the seeds are attached to the former and not to the latter.

Dry and dehiscent fruits which are composed of more than one carpel are 'capsular fruits'. The simplest form of capsule is formed from two carpels which join along their borders and make a unilocular ovary. In this class of capsule, the fruit is often divided into two locules by a film which is membranous and veinless and proceeds from the placentae, but it must be considered 'false' as it does not originate from the carpel walls. If these capsules are three times as long as they are broad, or even longer, they are called 'siliques'; those which are proportionately shorter, are 'silicles' or 'siliculae'. See Fig. 48. Except in unusual instances, siliques and silicles split along their edges, which come away from a kind of frame formed by the marginal veins. However, in exceptional cases they do not open by themselves but have to be opened, a phenomenon which is quite usual in the legumes. Siliques or the indehiscent legumes generally have more or less well marked bands where the fruit breaks up into one-seeded segments; such a pod is called a 'lomentum'.

Apart from follicles, legumes, siliques and silicles, we have 'capsules' *in sensu stricto*, with two or more carpels and dehiscing in various ways. If the fissures are longitudinal and coincide with the mid-rib of the carpel, the capsule is said to be 'loculicidal' (if the carpels are closed) because in this type of dehiscence the locules are destroyed. If the fissures are produced at the carpellary borders, also with the carpels closed, they are separate one from the other and the capsule is called 'septicidal' because the dissepiments (or partitions) are destroyed. And lastly, the capsules are 'septifragal' when the dissepiments are split down their length along several planes parallel to the axis of the fruit.

The septifragal capsule of the *Euphorbia*, or spurges, with their three monospermous cavities, have three different kinds of dehiscence. By septifragal dehiscence they become separated from the axis of the fruit and persist as three one-seeded locules; these three locules then separate from each other by septicidal dehiscence, and then by loculicidal dehiscence they open in two places to release their seeds. Such a fruit is called an 'elaterium'. There are also capsules which open transversally by means of a kind of lid or operculum; the lower part is shaped like an urn or vessel containing the seeds and is called a 'pyxidium'. The pimpernels (*Anagallis*) and the henbanes (*Hyoscyamus*) have pyxidia for fruit.

Among the dry and 'indehiscent fruits', the 'achenes' occupy first place. The achenes are dry fruits which do not open, and enclose a single seed in such a way that the pericarp is not fused to it but remains quite loose. Thus, they are fruits which can be peeled without doing damage either to the seed or the pericarp. There are many kinds of achenes, according to whether they have been formed from one or more carpels, from a superior or an inferior ovary, and according to the consistency of the pericarp. But, generally, the achene which is formed by only part of a carpellary leaf is called a 'nutlet', and examples are found in the Labiatae. In this family, and in the Boraginaceae, the ovary has two carpels and is divided into four achenes, forming a 'tetrachene'. Each one of these is formed from half a carpel only, and is therefore a nutlet.

The 'caryopsis' is the characteristic fruit of the grass family, and differs from the achene in that it has its pericarp closely stuck to the seed. If the achenes or the nutlet have a membranous prolongation rather like a wing, they are given the name of 'samaras'. The samara of the elm tree is very well known; it matures and falls from the tree before the leaves begin to shoot.

Between the dry fruits and the fleshy fruits we must find a place for the 'pomegranate'. The pomegranate is a curious type of fruit with a leathery pericarp composed of carpellary walls, with the receptacle deeply hollowed, the ovary being inferior, and with seeds—the edible part of the fruit—of fleshy episperm. It also has an inferior group of carpels with another group placed on top of them. The partitions are thin films formed from the membranes dividing the segments.

The simplest kind of 'fleshy fruit' is the 'drupe', formed from a single carpel and a single seed, and enclosed within a stony endocarp. The afore-mentioned peach, the cherries, plums, olives, etc., are all drupes. Many other stony fruits, formed from various combined carpels, and there-fore usually with several stones, are 'drupaceous fruits' known as 'nuculania'. If the endocarp is fleshy or pulpy, but without a stone, the fruit is called a 'berry'. Tomatoes are berries, and so are the fruits of *Belladonna* (deadly nightshade) and other Solanaceae. The fruits of citrus trees, such as oranges, lemons, grape-fruit, etc., are berries having singular characteristics. Normally, they are com-

posed of ten closed carpels—the 'sections' of the orange—
with membranous partitions, filled with large juicy cells.
The epicarp is rich in aromatic oils and essences and the
mesocarp is spongy, white and tasteless. This fruit is
called a 'hesperidium', from the Garden of the Hesperides.

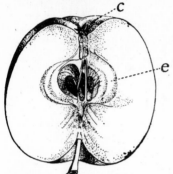

Fig. 49
Complex fruit of the apple,
called a 'pome', sectioned
longitudinally. At the top is
the calyx, *c*. The interior of
the fruit, the 'core', is divided
into five coriaceous locules
which, in carpological terminology, are referred to as the
endocarp, *e*. The edible portion
of the apple corresponds with
the receptacle, very swollen
and fleshy, at the heart of
which lies the real fruit.

The fruits of the apple and pear trees are called 'pomes',
and come from inferior ovaries. See Fig. 49. Because of
this they are quite complex, since the pericarp is composed
not only of the walls of the ovary, but also of the receptacle.
They have a fleshy mesocarp and a tough endocarp. The
seeds of the pomes are called 'pips'. Melons, calabashes
and cucumbers are called 'pepos', and in this category are
found the largest fruits, some calabashes weighing more
than fifty pounds. They also are complicated fruits, springing from inferior ovaries and from three to five carpels, and
having a pulpy endocarp sometimes reabsorbed by the
fruit itself, leaving a space inside. Among these fruits is
found the singular pepo, the quirting cucumber (*Ecballium
elaterium*) which is an explosive fruit. During the time it
is ripening, it fills gradually with juices under pressure,
and when the time comes for the fruit to fall, this pressure
causes the seeds, mixed with juice, to be shot a considerable distance through the hole left by the stalk.

MULTIPLE FRUITS. When the gynaeceum is composed of
independent carpels, not fused into a single body, they

form several separate fruits as they ripen. A group of monocarpellary fruits formed in this way is called a 'multiple fruit'. Thus, in the strawberry we have a convex receptacle, swollen and juicy at its maturity and containing numerous achenes attached to it—those tiny seeds dispersed over the surface. In the brambles or blackberries a cone of druplets is formed. In some species of larkspur, various follicles occur joined together, and so on. In these cases we are dealing with a 'polyachene', a 'multidrupe' and a 'plurifollicle', respectively—in a word, with various kinds of multiple fruits. The 'cynorrhodon' of rose bushes is also a polyachene, but with a fleshy, hollow receptacle which completely hides the true fruits.

INFRUCTESCENCES. Although inflorescences have their flowers arranged in a fairly regular fashion, fruits originating from inflorescences generally congregate in such a manner that together they constitute a single carpological unit. They differ from multiple fruits in that they do not spring from a single flower, but from several. Since they come from an inflorescence they are called 'infructescent'. The fruit of the common fig tree, the 'syconium', consists of a pear-shaped hollow receptacle on whose inner walls innumerable little unisexual flowers are formed. This fruit is not, then, a 'fruit', but an 'aggregate of fruits'—an infructescence. The true fruits, fertile or otherwise, are the small seeds which are found inside the fig. Other infructescences are the fruits of the white mulberry tree and the pineapple. This last is formed from numerous concrescent fruits, and topped by a crest of sterile bracts.

'FRUITS' OF THE GYMNOSPERMS. We put the word fruit in this case in inverted commas because, in the strict botanical sense of the word, fruits do not exist in the gymnosperms, for their carpellary leaves do not close to make ovaries and without ovaries they cannot form a fruit. But in actual fact they do produce something biologically equivalent to a fruit which has the ability to perform the same protective functions. If, instead of the pineapple, we were to consider the cone of the fir tree, we would see that they both originate from inflorescences; but the pineapple has flowers with ovaries and consequently is an authentic infructescence, while the cone is not because the carpels in it do not close. The cones of the conifers are called 'strobili'. Other structures, similar except that they are rounded or ovoid, and more or less fleshy, such as those of the junipers, are called 'galbulae'.

THE SEED. Seeds occur in both the gymnosperms and the angiosperms—that is to say, in all the 'spermatophyta'. It is the rudimentary seed with its fertilised ovule, in which has developed an incipient plant, but halted in its development and capable of remaining in a dormant state for a long or short period of time—sometimes for many years, sometimes for only a few days.

The plant in miniature contained within the seed is the embryo, which is composed of one, two or more cotyledons, the plumule and the radicle. There are embryos with their cotyledons well supplied with nourishment, such as the beans and peas; and others which lack reserves of nutriment.

The shapes and dimensions of seeds are most variable. In size they range from the coconut to the seeds of the orchids, which are so tiny that they have been compared with iron filings.

INDEX

128